The Lexicon Of Love
An ABC Of Delightful Depravity

The Lexicon Of Love
An ABC Of Delightful Depravity

Jo Richardson

Chrysalis
Impact

First published in 2002 by Chrysalis Impact,
An imprint of Chrysalis Books plc
64, Brewery Road,
London N7 9NT
United Kingdom

A member of Chrysalis Books plc
© 2002 Chrysalis Books plc

ISBN 1 84411 002 8

Volume © Chrysalis Books plc 2002

Credits
Commissioning editors: Will Steeds, Chris Stone
Project management: Jo Richardson
Designed by Grade Design Consultants, London
Colour reproduction: Anorax Imaging Ltd
Printed and bound in Spain

Acknowledgements
Much of this material first appeared in *The Erotic Review*
and Emily Ford's *Pillow Book*.
Special thanks to The DuPret Collection

About the Author

Jo Richardson is the author and editor of *The
Lexicon of Love*. She has spent her working life in
publishing: as an editor she has covered every genre
from crime fiction to embroidery and educational
textbooks to motorbikes. As an author she has
focused on the sensual pleasures of life from
aromatherapy and face painting to cookery and, of
course, sex. She is a Gemini and lives with her
husband by the sea.

The Lexicon Of Love

Contents

Foreword

A warm welcome from the Erotic Print Society

One evening in May 1985 a private view at a small gallery off Bond Street seemed to be attracting many more guests than usual. A ripple of excitement went through the visitors that spilt onto the pavement outside the Maclean Gallery: here was an exhibition with a difference. The crowd-pulling theme of this show was erotic art – including Indian miniatures of the 17th century with delicate and acrobatic copulating couples, 18th century Japanese shunga woodcuts, peopled by lovers with delightfully exaggerated sexual organs, watercolours of Regency bucks cavorting naked with rosy-cheeked maids while the languid lithographs of John Lennon brought us almost up to date. And almost unbelievably, it was the first exhibition of its kind in the UK – commercial or otherwise.

About ten years later the Erotic Print Society came into being. I stopped trying to be a serious art dealer and became, well, a frivolous pornographer, thinking that if anyone had to have the thoroughly self-sacrificing job of publishing these images it might as well be me. Initially we sold limited edition prints. These were popular among collectors, but letting them know about us was always difficult: many newspapers were, at first, unwilling to accept our advertisements. We started a popular newsletter for our collectors: *The Erotic Print Society Review*. I gratefully handed over the editorship to the beauteous Rowan Pelling. The newsletter became a magazine, its name changing to *The Erotic Review*. She now owns and publishes the magazine as a separate company, although we maintain very close and friendly ties.

Attitudes towards the consumption and enjoyment of erotica or pornography have changed significantly since that 1985 exhibition; people seem to be more confident in their sexuality, more demanding about the quality of what they read or look at. The Erotic Print Society now issues more books than prints (about twenty a year), though we still produce limited edition erotic prints for collecting and framing. The EPS range has expanded from erotic art to erotic photography and now, with our new imprint The Scarlet Library, we've produced a series of illustrated erotic classics.

The artists and photographers we publish are both historic and contemporary: we published the first two books of Victorian photographic pornography in the UK and held our breath to see what the authorities would think of them. They are still in print. While the work of well-established contemporary erotic artists such as Lynn Paula Russell, Tim Major and Sylvie Jones fills our catalogues we are constantly finding new artists to publish. The same applies to erotic photography: China Hamilton, Trevor Watson and Eric Wilkins all represent very different aspects of erotic photography. New names and themes are in the pipeline.

In this more liberal sexual climate, we recognise the need to explore many different aspects of the erotic: some exciting and new, some reassuring and familiar, some amusing and some challenging – but all of them thought-provoking and arousing. The Erotic Print Society has provided much of the material for this edition of *The Lexicon of Love*, and if you like our ideas and principles as publishers of sophisticated erotica, I hope you'll find time to visit us soon. Our details can be found on page 318 of this book.

James Maclean

James Maclean
Publisher, EPS

"A" is not a discreet letter; it's a bold, open-mouthed character and therefore provides the perfect opener for our Lexicon of Love. And "opening" is a key concept, as it were, in lovemaking. Here we explore an exciting array of As, from openings outdoors (Actirasty) to rear openings (Anal Antics).

Arousal Contrary to the Venus and Mars orthodoxy of recent times, men and women share much when it comes to sex, including the same stages of sexual response – desire, arousal, and climax. Physical or psychological stimulation triggers sexual desire, which in turn sets the blood flowing round the body, filling our sexually significant tissues. And yes, we even have erection in common; the vaginal tissues and lips as well as the clitoris become engorged with blood and swell in the same way as the penis. But our differences lie in what turns us on. Whatever new techniques and theories abound, women want foreplay but bolted into the right psychological framework. And whatever that is is down to the individual and up to them to create. He can then concentrate on pressing her favoured buttons.

Actirasty This obscure term applies to the phenomenon of being sexually turned on by the sun. How widespread this is and how powerful the response is open to conjecture. But the sun is undeniably inextricably associated with sex – witness the traditional package holiday sell of sun, sand, and sex. This hails a loosening if not abandonment of the normal codes of behaviour, not least of which is the legitimatization of near or total nudity in public (I like to toy with the ironic concept of going topless on the commuter train, weather permitting, naturally). Sure as hell, there is nothing as sensual as sunbathing in the buff (provided one's tender bits are suitably protected from the rays) followed by a skinny dip.

Acupressure A so-called "complementary" therapy (now upgraded in status from "alternative"), acupressure is one of the ancient Eastern systems of healing which focus on the well-being of the whole individual – spiritually and emotionally as well as physically – as opposed to the Western approach of first and foremost treating symptoms. The foundation of this particular practice is the belief that we are all fuelled by "vital energy" or "life force" called, in the various Eastern languages, *prana, chi, qi, or ki*, and that this is transported around the body in a map of channels known as meridian lines, along which are specific acupressure points (and elsewhere). The idea is to manipulate the flow of energy (speeding up, slowing down, or re-routing) by massaging certain points, depending on the part of the body to which they relate. It's acupuncture without the needles. Unlikely as it may seem, one of the most effective acupressure points for enhancing sexual energy in both men and women is in the foot – on the inside, just below/behind the ankle bone. Or try the back, particularly the small of the back, either side of the spine.

Tim Major

And the moral?

Kindness effects more than severity.

Tim Major

Andropause As you may have guessed if you didn't already know, this is the term for a recently introduced concept – the male menopause – or so I thought. But apparently it is rumoured to have first appeared in medical literature somewhere between the 1940s and early 1950s, which precisely mirrors the age range of men at risk of suffering the symptoms of andropause. The latter are not as severe as for the female menopause but they can occur over a number of years, and the andropause has no absolute, tangible calling card, such as the end of menstruation in women. The cause is the same – a decline in hormone levels; oestrogen in women, testosterone in men. It seems that the main reason why the idea has taken so long to catch on is that the symptoms have been rolled into the usual aging issues, especially the psychological anxieties that characterize the mid-life crisis. Symptoms include loss of sex drive, energy, and muscle strength, changes in mood and behaviour, and osteoporosis. As Mae West helpfully noted, "You're never too old to become younger".

Analingus More commonly known as "rimming", which is a graphic description of what can be involved. In fact, both terms usually cover licking and probing the "butthole" with the tongue. It's not surprising that the anus, both internally and externally, responds enthusiastically to stimulation, since it is so close to the sex organs proper, with their abundance of nerve endings. So what about technique? Teasing the rim with a rhythmic flick of the tongue is a nice approach, as is a regular thrusting of the tongue against the anus and away as if ringing a doorbell. And what of health concerns? There is a risk of spreading potentially harmful bacteria and infections, and some advisors caution against post-rimming oral sex or kissing. Unproven as a measure against infection is brushing and rinsing your mouth out with antiseptic mouthwash, but it sounds like a reasonable idea.

The Professional

*That neat **Asiatic**
acrobat who adopts
the most curious poses
is titillating to the fingertips.
I go for her. Not because
she knows every position
and every where to put
her feather hands, but because
she can get my poor withered
cock to stand. Doesn't mind
the shrunken skin.
She mouths it, teases
and clasps it,
and between her thighs
will warm up a stand
in Hell's frozen flames.*

Automedon (from the Greek)

Peter Fendi (1796–1842)

Rojan (20th Century)

A is for Anal

Anal Antics

Victoria Grahame

From *Memoirs of a Woman of Pleasure*, by "Fanny Hill" – **John Cleland**

"He leads me to the table, and with a master-hand lays my head down on the edge of it, and with the other canting up my petticoat and shift, bares my naked posterior to his blind and furious guide: it forces its way between them, and I, feeling pretty sensibly that it was going by the right door and knocking desperately at the wrong one, I told him of it: 'Pooh,' says he 'my dear, any port in a storm'."

This is possibly the most famous literary reference to an attempt at buggery. Fanny, if you don't already know, eventually guides her sailor consort home to dock in the more conventional port, her vagina. It is the nonchalance with which he greets her announcement that he is about to sodomize her unintentionally which is so interesting. As far as I (and many of those to whom I've spoken on the subject) know, the practice of anal sex is far from "any port in a storm". No, it arouses far more passionate responses than that, be they positive or not.

Rebecca, a girl I have been close to since school, is a case in point. Her introduction to anal has been a Damascus style-conversion: she, quite literally, *saw the dark*. When contemporaries at our Roman Catholic school – which had the highest teenage pregnancy rate in the region – began to embark on their first sexual encounters, Rebecca was horrified to learn of a rumour that was circulating about her classmate and neighbour, Louise. "She let her boyfriend *put it up her bottom*," she whispered. I simply shrugged, not because I was a cool and sexually precocious fifth former, but because I don't think I actually knew what she was talking about. Rebecca was particularly traumatized as she had let the adolescent couple use her bedroom to "talk" in when her parents went out for the evening. Ass-fucking came to be a topic of horrid fascination and moral disbelief for Rebecca. Years later at a raucous hen night, one of the party produced a double-pronged vibrator in the shape of a thumb and forefinger moulded in plastic. Confidently, Rebecca spouted, "You can't get two girls onto this – the thingies are too near each other." When the other girls pointed out that the "thingies", or probes, were not designed for two women to mount, but to fit into the holes of one, she went pale with mortification. Standing her ground she replied, "No, it *can't* be". Like Queen Victoria's lesbians, for Rebecca, devotees of anal pleasure simply didn't exist. I assume that she just wasn't that way inclined and that any boyfriend's exploratory fingers (doubtless there had been attempts) around her rim had received short shrift. But she was still vocal about her disdain for the activity until one night when she tried Ecstasy and had her puckered anus thoroughly ploughed by an Australian barman she was seeing. A male friend, John, colludes with Rebecca's explanation that the right time, place, and man can make all the difference. John insists that he's not a bullish back-door man, but that once he'd met the girl who he thought might give it a go, he immediately manoeuvred his fingers into her tighter hole to gauge his chances of getting his cock in there too. Like Rebecca, John's girlfriend was resistant in the extreme, but came almost on the instant she was impaled.

According to Rebecca, the product of Irish immigrants, being brought up in a Catholic culture produces mixed feelings about anal sex; the sin of Sodom is also a widely practised form of contraception in devout countries as barrier, chemical, and surgical methods are all strictly forbidden. Italian men, donkey-schlonged Rocco Siffredi amongst them, are reputedly more focused on the penetration of the female bottom than any other sexual practice. I am hesitant to write off a whole nation as anally obsessed, lest I should make enemies, but a good friend of mine who is engaged to a Sicilian says that it's true, or at least that her fiancé "is a bit of a bottomite". In my experience, men of all origins are curious about the dark star, but as to whether it is novel or normal could possibly be attributed to ethnicity. A "Roman engagement" is a slang term for anal intercourse with a female virgin. In *Lady Chatterley's Lover*, Mellors takes liberties with milady's arsehole that her husband, Sir Clifford, describes as Italianate: "If a man likes to use his wife, as Benvenuto Cellini says, 'in the Italian way', well that is a matter of taste. But I had hardly expected our game-keeper to be up to so many tricks." While we're on the subject of differing global attitudes to anal, I'm reliably informed that it's the common Brazilian man's ultimate sexual fantasy to "fuck a blonde up the arse". Presumably, if there's a post-colonial reading to be had, this desire spreads beyond just South America. Actually, who doesn't want to fuck a blonde up the arse? I would if I could.

The concept that sodomy can be employed as a method of preserving maidenhood has surfaced more than once during my research. My colleague tells me that at her university many Greek girls practised only sodomy with their boyfriends in order to hold on to virginity for the marriage bed

(and of course "Greek" features heavily in slang phrases for anal, though more often than not, homosexual). Angela Carter writes in *The Sadeian Woman* of the gang-rape of Sade's *Justine*. Justine implores the participants to spare her hymen and so is subject to multiple buggery, Carter says, "…obeying the letter if not the spirit of her request, they strip her, sexually abuse her, and ejaculate upon her body… Her unruptured hymen is a visible sign of her purity, even if her breasts and belly have been deluged in spunk."

Perversely, if the practice has a reputation for being Catholic and continental European, it is also condemned for its contraceptive, and therefore unnatural, use. "Sodomy" was once a generic term for any sexual behaviour that involved ejaculation without the possibility of conception; anal, oral, bestiality, pederasty, even.

Like oral pleasure, anal is *extra* – not necessary for reproduction, and therefore against nature. The primary objection that women have to butt-fucking is that it is "dirty", and surely a woman's backside is simply not designed to have a rigid phallus inserted into it, never mind have it repeatedly thrust to the point of orgasm in there, so surely anal sex is too painful to be "normal"? All three are arguments against conquering the dark star, but all, in my opinion, make anal absolutely necessary in a sexual partnership. In response to the first charge, well, yes, it's unnatural, but so is kissing if you want to take it that far. As for painful and "dirty", the back passage may not be designed for reproductive intercourse, but in a clean and lubricious condition, that canal can give and receive considerable pleasure. The idea that it should be written off purely because it's painful is, I think, lacking in foresight. For a woman to complain that sodomy "will hurt too much" to try it is peculiar. *Straight* sex is, after all, initially painful. The teenage virgin suffers rupture and sometimes bleeding when she casts off her innocence. Women are, unfortunately, accustomed to discomfort: labour pains, which come about as a result of straightforward copulation, are, I imagine a goddamn-sight more painful than a stiff prick in the arse. With some perseverance, this sweet entry can be made love to without soreness and only irritation of an exquisite kind.

That is not, however, an excuse for you gentlemen to charge at your partner's cavity with this article in one hand and a hard cock in the other. It's not for everyone, but it's something which can grow on one given time. I must admit, it's not something I myself needed any persuasion with and was remarkably lucky to have a curious but tender lover for my first time, who himself was also a virgin. He massaged my behind and loosened me with lubrication and adventurous fingers, and slowly over a matter of several nights, introduced his stiff prick to my cunt's narrower neighbour.

A colleague who has not had "the pleasures of the back door", asked me what anal sex is like. Truthfully, I have to say that it is extremely physically pleasurable in my case. I think it feels exactly as the eponymous heroine of beating-and-buggery romp *Beatrice* describes it to her sister: "Your bottom cheeks are deliciously elastic, Caroline. The first time you will experience considerable tightness, but you will yield. You will feel the veins, the knob, the inpushing – the breath will explode from your lungs. But on the second bout, my sweet, your rosehole will receive the repeated pistoning of the cock until you have drawn forth his spurting juice."

After an evening's viewing of Rocco Siffredi's *True Anal Stories*, my lover and I discussed the attraction of "the Italian way". I suggested that the attraction for men was psychological rather than physical. Naturally he contested this, maintaining that the smaller passage was of course tighter, but admitted that "a man would put his dick in almost anything warm and wet". As for my claim that it was primarily a mental satisfaction for a man to gain entry to that hole, he agreed that there is a desire, a controllable one at that, to be permitted into the forbidden place because, by allowing it, the woman is submitting to him. OK, what he actually said was, "It's nice to fuck the arse off a girl", but I imagine he was trying to summarize what Nancy Friday said in *Men In Love*: "The anus becomes the most forbidden part of the body, thus invested with its own secret glamour." For a man, to penetrate her there is to therefore reduce her to his level of animality. Is that why overgrown schoolboys and rugby players say things like, "One up the bum, no harm done"? Whatever the hell that's supposed to mean.

"B" is a pushy character, thrusting its double protrusions to the fore. Not surprising then that it lays claim to all those body bits that echo its characteristics — Breasts, Buttocks and Balls. This is in-your-face eroticism, whether it's Bush or BD.

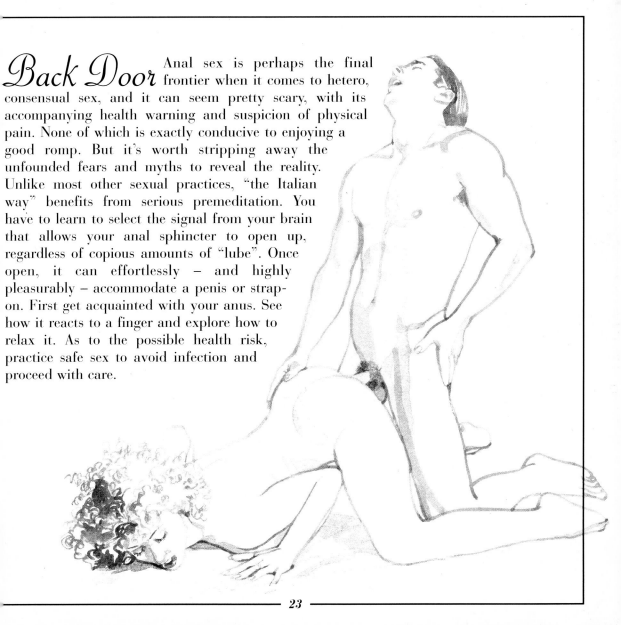

Back Door

Anal sex is perhaps the final frontier when it comes to hetero, consensual sex, and it can seem pretty scary, with its accompanying health warning and suspicion of physical pain. None of which is exactly conducive to enjoying a good romp. But it's worth stripping away the unfounded fears and myths to reveal the reality. Unlike most other sexual practices, "the Italian way" benefits from serious premeditation. You have to learn to select the signal from your brain that allows your anal sphincter to open up, regardless of copious amounts of "lube". Once open, it can effortlessly – and highly pleasurably – accommodate a penis or strap-on. First get acquainted with your anus. See how it reacts to a finger and explore how to relax it. As to the possible health risk, practice safe sex to avoid infection and proceed with care.

BD Bondage and domination go together hand in cuff, with, to use the proper terminology, "the Top" doing the dominating by restraining "the Bottom". To the uninitiated, this whole concept may appear at least bizarre and at worst deeply alarming and offputting, especially in the face of BD's associated paraphernalia – ropes (macramé just had to be revived some time), chains, spreader bars, shackles, hoods, gags, masks… But these are the mere props of a psychological drama, often carefully and ingeniously scripted and staged by the players. The very fact of assuming a role signals a release of self and therefore a suspension of "normal" rules, which all adds up to a freeing of inhibition. It's fairly obvious to perceive the attractions of being "the Top" – all that intoxicating power. But "the Bottom" has its own peculiar allure – a relinquishing of control leading to an absolution of responsibility; a wonderfully liberating state of mind. Those who find themselves constantly in a position of power in their everyday working lives can find this especially appealing.

Bizarre This pioneering fetish magazine, published during the 1940s and 1950s in the US, was mostly the work of one man, John Alexander Scott Coutts, under the choice pseudonym of John Willie. Now viewed as the father of modern fetishism, Willie penned such regular gems as "Footwear Fantasia" (by "Achilles"), illustrated with his beguiling photographs of women in buttoned thigh-length boots and cripplingly high-heeled shoes; "Figure Training", featuring some extreme forms of corsetry complete with surgical braces, and the infamous "Sir d'Arcy d'Arcy" strip cartoon starring the oft bound and gagged Sweet Gwendoline. Alongside readers' letters (one such from "The Chained Letter Writer") are occasional pieces on items of correction (and not just of deportment), such as "The Mask of Birchdale" and "The Scold's Bridle" ("Don't nag – by order"). Another classic feature was the following warning accompanying a different photograph in each issue of a model depicted Houdini-style: "Don't let this happen to you…learn Jiu-Jitsu and the art of self defense."

Bush To depilate or not to depilate, that is the burning question. There is an ancient precedent for the "bare beaver" or the pube-free cock and balls dating back to the Egyptians and the Greeks. Following a defiant reassertion of the natural look spearheaded by the feminist movement, we are now seeing a swing in favour of smooth. Either way, pubic haircare is no longer a minority beauty routine. Salons offer a choice of waxing styles for women, including the widely renowned Brazilian or Mohican for those concerned not to reveal a single stray pube in the inciest, winciest beachwear, while The Hollywood denotes the full monty. For those who have yet to take the plunge, there may be the concern that a bush makeover is an irreversible step, but it grows back just as before (if a little wilder) after an initially itchy stage. The consensus of opinion is that keeping hairless heightens sexual sensitivity for both her and him, and enhances the tactile pleasure of oral sex.

Butt Plugs and Beads These are the playthings of the anal sex aficionados. Butt plugs are cleverly and necessarily designed to attach themselves to the exterior via a flared base (haven't you heard the one about the woman who was using her mobile phone and ended up in A&E saying she'd slipped and fell on it in the shower). They give men an extra buzz by stimulating the prostate gland – the male G-spot – as well as the anus. Choose from silicone or vinyl (non-porous), or the dazzlingly coloured and texturally teasing jelly; long and slim or short and squat; with or without vibrator; expandable (by inflation) or no. Beads come strung together, some evenly sized, some graduating, in standard or large, with a ring pull. The idea is to remove them one by one just before climaxing, or, for a more dramatic effect, to whip them out on the point of orgasm.

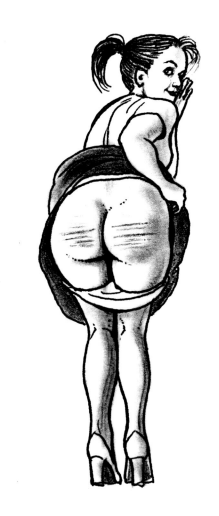

No **Bush** or Nae Hair On't

Yestereen I wed a lady fair,
And ye wad believe me,
On her cunt there grows nae hair,
That's the thing that grieves me.
It vexed me sair, it plagued me sair,
It put me in a passion
To think that I had wed a wife
Whose cunt was out o' fashion.

Anon (18th century), collected by Robert Burns

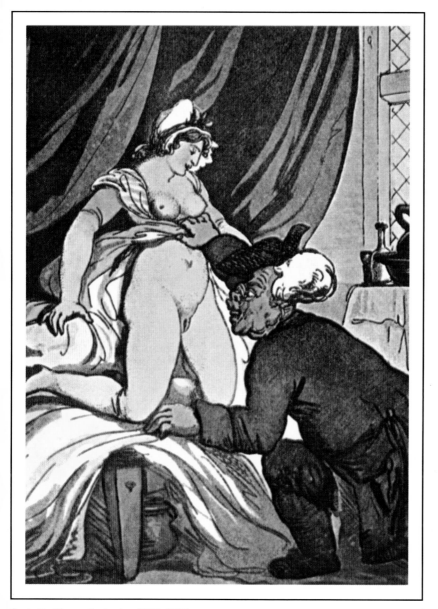

Curiosity, Thomas Rowlandson (1756–1827)

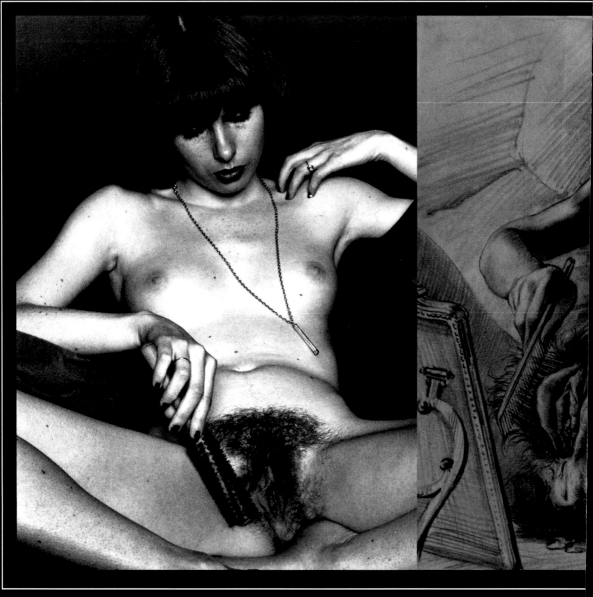

Eric Wilkins (Contemporary)   *Tom Poulton (20th Century)*

B is for Bisexual

Best of Both Worlds

Kate Copstick

Whenever someone asks me to define my sexuality nowadays, I always get a flashback to a September night I spent in an overpriced London hotel room, with nothing on except a Rocco Siffredi DVD and my gorgeous black strap-on. I was buggering a boy called John whom I had picked up in a gay bar.

Somehow it felt much more natural (feel free to disagree) to use my ersatz inches to part the buttocks of this admittedly somewhat less than macho young man than to plunge it into the pinker parts of a woman. But where, I mused as I thrusted and plunged until the fronts of my thighs slapped the backs of his, did that leave me on the colour chart of sexuality?

The accepted choice for a girl is simplistic...

Heterosexual – which is like being in Alba in autumn and never eating truffles.

Lesbian – which is like gagging for a cup of tea in Tokyo and having to go through the entire bloody tea ceremony before you can get one.

Or bisexual – which is like living in London and being able to have anything you want and order it in to boot.

I have always been with Sir Laurence on the "snails and oysters" question...I like both. So I am self-evidently bisexual. But what kind of bisexual am I? The question had occurred to me in the hotel room when the lovely and very obliging John turned the strap-on on me.

I do have problems with some aspects of bisexuality.

Women, mainly.

Don't get me wrong – I adore women. The first "whole body" sexual experience I had was with a female. Fifteen and led entirely by instinct, my tongue found its way from her mouth, in a direct line down the openings in her clothing, to its natural home between her legs. I can remember the taste and the sensation still. Sweet and musky softness under a fuzz of soft new-grown hair. And her breasts – both soft and firm, like two little clenched iron fists in velvet gloves. A perfect handful each.

And the women I have had since – young women with neat, sweet, pink, rosebud cunts that need nibbling and licking like little buttered corncobs, and older women with lush, louche, peony-rose cunts...the kind of ripe watermelon cunt you can lose almost your entire face in – each can erect my clit with just her memory.

In France I even found I enjoyed fat female flesh (well, my New Year's Resolution that year had been to try, each month, something I had never done before and, after February's "first", at the Singles' Dinner, nothing frightened me) when the kind of woman whom Rubens would have asked to lose weight approached me round the back of a bus (yes, I could just tell the difference). There is something sexy about that much flesh on a female. All those curves, all that smoothness. A body to spread oneself across instead of wrapping oneself around. At the risk of sounding Oedipal – a huge motherfucker. Great breasts that spill over hands like seven pounds of prime meat in a bag and yet, still, a cute, pert-lipped, two-finger cunt. Like finding a sweetie in a duvet.

Yes, all my lips quiver at the thought of a woman. But – and I am a butt girl – when I want an honest-to-goodness, goosepimple-erecting, eyewatering fuck, then I have to have a man.

Even a woman with a strap-on doesn't do it, despite having the kind of erection only naturally available with a mindless adolescent attached.

It is partly the power thing. Fucking is not a caring activity. People don't fuck. Bodies do. And arguably only bits of bodies do. I want a great big hard cock in my cunt...or ass...I do NOT want "you inside me". I want to be used. I will get embarrassed if you murmur my name. I want to be a sex object.

And women – generally – have a basic problem with objectification.

Men, on the other hand...

Like Julie Andrews, when I'm feeling sad, I simply remember my favourite things...the frighteningly right wing chap I met in the Groucho Club when both of us were dining with someone else. He murmured the magic words "you have a great ass" as I passed his table for a second time.

A bottle of champagne later, I was in a shoulder stand at North Clapham while he sank his dick into me like a pestle pounding into a mortar while chanting "fuck you fuck you fuck you"...the theatre technician who walked into my dressing room, announced: "I really want to fuck you" and had me on my hands and knees and in full Red Queen regalia in front of the "mirror, mirror on my wall"...the gloriously endowed gentleman I met in the Lounge Car of the overnight train from Glasgow to London and in whose Executive First compartment I enjoyed seconds, thirds, and got more cock in my mouth than a fox in a poultry farm...a wonderfully athletic American whose catchphrase was "shut up bitch and open your mouth".

I have only once had impersonal, body-bruising, pure-driven sex with a woman. She bit me, she chewed on my pussy...she played KitKat with my ass (that's four fingers...) Oddly, she thought she was straight. Not that night.

But I digress...OK, "deviate" is arguably *le mot juste...*

Quickies. Women have an underdeveloped appreciation of the quickie. The stand-up, no names, no talking, itch-scratching, thirst-quenching fuck.

When I am horny and I just want my cunt or my ass filled and fucked and finished off, I have generally found it to be men that will do that for me. I once had in my life a fabulous man amongst whose many, many fine points was his habit of saying – as we reached the front door *en route* to cinema, restaurant, or theatre... "Fancy a quickie before we go?"

I have never had a woman like that.

I am well aware that a bit of girl-on-girl action is what feeds the fantasies of most heterosexual men. But, let's face it chaps, you don't think that girl-play is sex: it is just very pretty foreplay. But nothing like the real thing. It needs a man to complete it, right? Wrong.

Although I have to admit to some great threesomes.

But the woman has to be genuinely bisexual.

Samantha was. And she had the great advantage of the callousness of the eighteen-year-old.

We met at a party, collected a *prima facie* alpha male, and made for the master bedroom where he greeted the conversing quartet there with the immortal words, "We're going to have sex now, you can stay if you want". They didn't. Maybe that was pretty close to perfect…a cock in my ass and a pussy in my face. And an unspoken agreement that the exchange of body fluids need not lead to an exchange of phone numbers.

I think that that, for me, is the factor. I can't say whether sex with men or sex with women is better. They are so different. Sex with women makes me come…maybe even more than sex with men. But what I hate is that women always CARE that I've come.

The best sex is pure sex. Not sex complicated by emotion, by history, by personalities, by caring. Just sex.

And that seems to take a man.

PS Any woman who would like to prove me wrong, please contact The Erotic Print Society and ask for my number.

"*C*", with its front entrance, is a receptive letter and cradles within it that precious pink rosebud of desire, the *Clitoris* — in much the same way as the mouth in the time-honoured art of *Cunnilingus*. *Coitus* is another word to enjoy getting your mouth around.

Cunnilingus Another awkward word to get your tongue around, which perhaps mirrors the challenges of the act itself. From the Latin, it literally means "cunt tonguing", which tells only half the story. Brushing, with closed lips, sucking, slobbering and eating are all on the agenda, but it's a very personal choice for the recipient as to what works with which bit – labia, clitoris, entrance to the vagina – and in what pace of rhythm and degree of pressure, particularly in relation to the clitoris. These requirements may of course change when the stage of arousal progresses, from delicate indirect flicking of the tongue to firmer, direct stimulation of the clitoris. Well, we women never pretended to be easily satisfied!

Cheesecake The term "Cheesecake", as the female equivalent of "Beefcake", entered the public domain as early as 1905, and came to denote commerically produced images of scantily clad women that managed not to affront the accepted standards of decency. Cheesecake was the personification of the wholesome, guilelessly seductive "girl next door", and its demarcation between the provocative and the pornographic survived well into the 1950s, despite the shedding of more and more attire. The 1930s heralded its heyday with *Esquire* magazine's "Petty Girl", realistically rendered in colour illustrations by George Petty, to be replaced in the 1940s by the even glossier Varga Girl, supremely executed by Albert Vargas. Meanwhile, cheesecake poses of that most beloved of 1950s pinups, Betty Grable, were helping the Allies win the war. But it was Bettie Page, leading light of photographer Irving Klaw's *Movie Star News*, who was the Playmate to end all *Playboy* Playmates, even following Norma Jean's infamous outing. Cheesecake found its way into every kind of printed matter, from calendars, postcards, and notepads to record sleeves.

Cock Rings Its long-standing as a sex aid may be testament to its efficacy but some of the claims made of the humble cock ring could be exaggerated – for instance, the ability to combat premature ejaculation. But exaggeration is the name of the game here. Dubbed the poor man's Viagra, cock rings enhance size and hardness, and can help make a bigger erection last for longer. Some rings fit solely around the base of the penis (and can incorporate varying kinds of clitoris stimulator), but many are designed to wrap around the balls as well as the base of the shaft. The fixed metal variety, fitted on to the flaccid member, are not to be undertaken lightly, given that they can't be immediately removed if causing pain; size very much matters in this case. Some more complex and extreme contraptions are available for use in SM. Less scary are the rubber stretch-ons or the extra-flexible jelly rings and the adjustable, snap-on (and off) leather affairs. The bondage connotations can only enhance the experience.

Coitus à Mammilla

Otherwise known as Bombay roll, boob-balling, or, best of all, jug-joisting. If you are a breast man, thrusting to orgasm in your lover's cleavage is likely to be especially appealing, but it's an erotic notion by any standards. For the woman's part, if you are particularly well-endowed (naturally or surgically), chances are that any opportunity to flaunt and wield your prized possessions will be enthusiastically grasped at. Squeezing and massaging them as you control your hold on him, together with the feel of his taut scrotum pushing up against them, has undeniable attractions.

Cross-dressing

So where does cross-dressing stop and transvestism begin? In either case, this is predominantly a male preserve and a hetero one at that, but is it all to do with the pursuit of sexual pleasure? Certainly, the textbook definition of a transvestite is someone specifically motivated to cross-dress for the purposes of getting turned on. Non-sexual cross-dressers would appear to be those men who are drawn to assume the woman's mantle, for limited periods, as a source of comfort and emotional fulfilment. Also, there are those wanting to experience the indulgence of self-pampering and unashamed preening that remains mostly a woman's prerogative, which may carry an undercurrent of sensuality. Then there is the overtly sexual cross-dressing of SM sex game fame. Transvestites are perhaps defined by their compulsive desire to appropriate female dress and behaviour, persistently and in public. But not as the "litttle woman" next door; rather the diva or the businesswoman, the tart or the nun – the enactment of a fantasy in stereotypical style.

Me Husband's Got No **Courage** in Him

Me husband's admired wherever he goes
And everyone looks well upon him
With his handsome features and well-shaped leg
But still he's got no **courage** in him.

Me husband can dance and caper and sing
And do anything that's fitting for him
But he cannot do the thing I want
Because he's got no courage in him.

All sorts of vittles I did provide
All sorts of meats that's fitting for him
With oyster pie and rhubarb too
But still he's got no courage in him.

Every night when I goes to bed
I lie and throw one leg right o'er him
And me hand I clamp between his thighs
But I can't put any courage in him.

Seven long years I've made his bed
And every night I've lain beside him
But this morning I rose with me maidenhead
For still he's got no courage in him.

I wish me husband he was dead
And in his grave I'd quietly lay him
And then I'd find another one
That had a little courage in him.

So all ye maids come listen to me
Don't marry a man before you've tried him
Or else you'll sing this song like me
Me husband's got no courage in him.

Traditional song

The Old Man, *Thomas Rowlandson (1756–1827)*

Eric Wilkins (Contemporary)

C is for Dangers of *Coitus*

Of matters which are injurious in the act of generation

Extract from *The Perfumed Garden*

Know, O Vizir (to whom God be good!), that the ills caused by coition are numerous. I will mention to you some of them, which to know is essential, in order to be able to avoid them.

Let me tell you in the first place that coition, if performed standing, affects the knee-joints and brings about nervous shiverings; and if performed sideways will predispose your system for gout and sciatica, which resides chiefly in the hip joint.

Do not mount upon a woman fasting or immediately before making a meal, or else you will have pains in your back, you will lose your vigour, and your eyesight will get weaker.

If you do it with the woman bestriding you, your dorsal cord will suffer and your heart will be affected; and if in that position the smallest drop of the usual secretions of the vagina enters your urethral canal, a painful stricture may supervene.

Do not leave your member in the vulva after ejaculation, as this might cause gravel, or softening of the vertebral column, or the rupture of blood vessels, or, lastly, inflammation of the lungs.

Too much exercise after coition is also detrimental.

Avoid washing your member after the copulation, as this may cause canker.

As to coition with old women, it acts like a fatal poison, and it has been said, "Do not rummage old women, were they as rich as Karoun". And it has further been said, "Beware of mounting old women; even if they cover you with favours". And again, "The coitus of old women is a venomous meal".

Know that the man who works a woman younger than he is himself acquires new vigour; if she is of the same age as he is he will derive no advantage from it; and, finally, if it is a woman older than himself she will take all his strength out of him for herself.

The excessive practice of coition injures the health on account of the expenditure of too much sperm. For as butter made of cream represents the quintessence of the milk, and if you take the cream off, the milk loses its qualities, even so does the sperm form the quintessence of nutrition, and its loss is debilitating. On the other hand, the condition of the body, and consequently the quality of the sperm, depends directly upon the food you take. If, therefore, a man will passionately give himself up to the enjoyment of coition, without undergoing too great a fatigue, he must live upon strengthening food, exciting comfits, aromatic plants, meat, honey, eggs, and other similar viands. He who follows such a regime is protected against the following accidents, to which excessive coition may lead.

Firstly, the loss of generative power.

Secondly, the deterioration of his sight; for although he may not become blind, he will at least have to suffer from eye diseases if he does not follow my advice.

Thirdly, the loss of his physical strength; he may become like the man who wants to fly but cannot, who pursuing somebody cannot catch him, or who carrying a burden, or working, soon gets tired and prostrated.

He who does not want to feel the necessity for coition uses camphor. Half of a *mitskal* of this substance, macerated in water, makes the man who drinks of it insensible to the pleasures of copulation. Many women use this remedy when in fits of jealousy against rivals, or when they need repose after great excesses. Then they try to procure camphor that has been left after a burial, and shrink from no expense of money to get such from the old women who have the charge of the corpses. They also make use of the flower of henna, which is called *faria*; they macerate the same in water, until it turns yellow, and thus supply themselves with a beverage which has almost the same effect as camphor.

I have treated of these remedies in the present chapter, although this is not their proper place; but I thought that this information, as here given, may be of use to many persons.

There are certain things which will become injurious if constantly indulged in and which in the end affect the health. Such are: too much sleep, long voyages in unfavourable season, which latter, particularly in cold countries, may weaken the body and cause disease of the spine. The same effects may arise from the habitual handling of those bodies which engender cold and humidity, like plaster, etc.

For people who have difficulty in passing water, coitus is hurtful.

The habit of consuming acid food is debilitating.

To keep one's member in the vulva of a woman after ejaculation has taken place, be it for a long or a short time, enfeebles that organ and makes it less fit for coition.

If you are lying with a woman, do her business several times if you feel inclined, but take care not to overdo it, for it is a true word that, "He who plays the game of love for his own sake, and to satisfy his desires, feels the most intense and durable pleasure; but he who does it to satisfy the lust of another person will languish, lose all his desire, and finish by becoming impotent for coition".

The sense of these words is that a man when he feels disposed for it can give himself up to the exercise of coitus with more or less ardour according to his desires, and at the time which best suits him, without any fear of future impotence, if his enjoyment is provoked and regulated only by his feeling the want of lying with a woman.

But he who makes love for the sake of somebody else, that is to say only to satisfy the passion of his mistress, and tries all he can to attain that impossibility, that man will act against his own interest and imperil his health to please another person.

As injurious may be considered coition in the

bath or immediately after leaving the bath; after having been bled or purged or such like. Coitus after a heavy bout of drinking is likewise to be avoided. To indulge coitus with a woman during her courses is as detrimental to the man as to the woman herself, as at that time her blood is vitiated and her womb cold, and if the least drop of blood should get in the man's urinary canal numerous maladies may supervene. As to the woman, she feels no pleasure during her courses, and at such time holds coitus in aversion.

As regards copulation in the bath, some say that there is no pleasure to be derived from it, if, as is believed, the degree of enjoyment is dependent upon the warmth of the vulva; for in the bath the vulva cannot be otherwise than cold, and consequently unfit for giving pleasure. And it is besides not to be forgotten that the water penetrating into the sexual parts of man or woman may lead to grave consequences.

Coitus after a full meal may occasion rupture of the intestines. It is also to be avoided after undergoing much fatigue, or at a time of very hot or very cold weather.

Amongst the accidents which may attend the act of coition in hot countries may be mentioned sudden blindness without any previous symptoms.

The repetition of the coitus without washing the parts ought to be shunned, as it may enfeeble the virile power.

The man must also abstain from copulation with his wife if he is in a state of legal impurity, for if she should become pregnant by such coition the child could not be sound.

After ejaculation do not remain close to the woman, as the disposition for recommencing will suffer by doing so.

Care is to be taken not to carry heavy loads on one's back or to over-exert the mind, if one does not want the coitus to be impeded. It is also not good constantly to wear vestments made of silk, as they impair all the energy for copulation.

Silken cloths worn by women also affect injuriously the capacity for erection of the virile member.

Fasting, if prolonged, calms sexual desire; but in the beginning it excites the same.

Abstain from greasy liquids, as in the course of time they diminish the strength necessary for coition.

The effect of snuff, whether plain or scented, is similar.

It is bad to wash the sexual parts with cold water directly after copulation; in general, washing with cold water calms down the desire, while warm water strengthens it.

Conversation with a young woman excites in a man the erection and passion commensurate with the youthfulness of the woman.

"D" may stand with its back to the wall but its sexual delights come from behind — in Dildo, Doggy style, and the delicious Derrière itself. But Desire can come from any quarter. However, there's a sting in the tail — beware the Dominatrix!

Doggy Style

This is mating, pure and simple, and as such has its particular attractions when you want it hot, deep, and strong; it's the very base, animalistic quality of the coupling that provides the real excitement. Rather than being merely submissive, she kneels on all fours to expose and flaunt her genitalia. He "covers" her, even grasping the scruff of her neck – reminiscent of, say, a male leopard that holds on to his mate's neck with his teeth. Using the leverage of her hands on the bed, or wherever (carpets, depending on their quality, are fine if you enjoy the added *frisson* of pain from friction burns), she can push back on to him, grinding her buttocks into his groin.

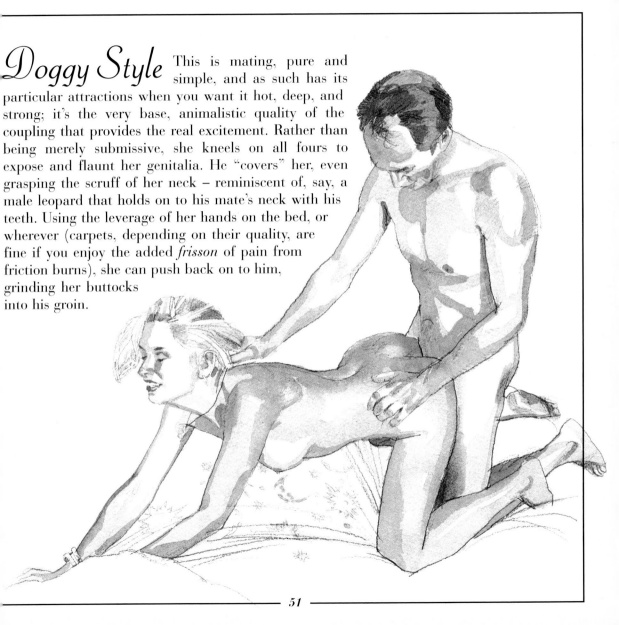

Deep Throat The dramatization of this hitherto relatively obscure not to say challenging oral technique was released upon an unsuspecting public in 1972 in the film of the same name which, despite being deemed obscene by the state of New York and numerous attempts to ban it, was widely screened. It went on to become the most successful blue movie ever. If the basic plot has passed you by, it centres on a woman, played by Linda Lovelace (Boreman) whose only means of sexual satisfaction is to take a man's penis into her throat, since that's where her clitoris is located. Which she duly does, starting with the doctor who has successfully diagnosed her condition. Boreman, who died in April 2002, later alleged that not only was she was forced into performing some of the scenes at gunpoint (by her husband) but that she didn't get paid. Her subsequent move into anti-pornography campaigning comes as no surprise. The "feat" itself requires considerable practice to learn how to disengage the gag reflex and to swallow the penis slowly and gently.

D'Eon, Chevalier/e Charles d'Eon de Beaumont has been coined the patron saint of transvestites; in fact, his name has given us eonism, a term for men who adopt female attire and behaviour. In his memoirs, D'Eon says that he was born female (in Burgundy in 1728) but brought up as male. Skipping over his early life, we find "him" working for Louis XV in his spy network, who sends him on a diplomatic mission to the court of Empress Elizabeth of Russia, during which time he dons women's clothes to facilitate negotiations. Diplomatic relations successfully restored, he exchanges his frock for the Captain of the Dragoons uniform, fights a decent campaign, and is duly decorated. After a diplomatic posting-cum-spying mission to London ends in tears, during which time bets on his gender are big business, we find him back in France as a woman, officially declared by Louis XVI. He later returns to England, where "she" takes up fencing (in petticoats) to earn a crust, even fighting the Prince of Wales. All bets were off, however, in 1810 when a postmortem revealed that D'Eon had been a man after all.

Dildo   I have read varying accounts of the dildo down the ages, and while it's difficult to be certain as to what is historically accurate, it would seem that the false phallus has been around for some considerable time – reputedly over 30,000 years. It pops up in a variety of guises, fashioned from wood or formed from stalks and tied to the waist in the *Kama Sutra*; impressive jade and ivory items in Ancient China; a padded leather version complete with olive oil "lube" in the Hellenstic Age; even, supposedly, made from dried camel dung sealed with resin in the Middle East of yore. Hooray for latex! We can now pleasure ourselves, in whichever orifice, with a range of sophisticated models, including those with quasi realistic-looking (and -feeling) balls and veining, some with handy suction cups for fixing to a hard surface; double "dongs" that consist of two dildos joined end to end for two people to use simultaneously (with practice); plus a whole range of strap-ons with adjustable harnesses to hold the dildo firmly in place and optional vibrator.

Dominatrix   A dominatrix is a skilled professional – a mistress of the art of fantasy, role-play, bondage, discipine techniques, and fetish-dressing. But the one thing she definitely doesn't have on offer is sex. A creative dominatrix, on the other hand, will be able to explore and fulfil your individual erotic fantasies but also be able to bring something new and unexpected to the experience. Operating from her "dungeon", as it is known in the trade, she will have to hand such delights as a cage, stocks, or whipping bench, or maybe an examination table or dentist's chair, depending on your particular preference. And at her disposal she will doubtless have a wardrobe of outfits ready and waiting to help realize your perfect sub/dom scenario. But have no real fear – a safe or release word will be agreed at the beginning of the session as an exit. Visiting a dominatrix as a couple can offer the chance of expanding and enhancing your repertoire of sex mind games.

Desire...

Naked she lay, clasped in my longing arms,
I filled with love, and she all over charms;
　Both equally inspired with eager fire,
Melting through kindness, flaming in **desire**.
With arms, legs, lips close clinging to embrace,
She clips me to her breast and sucks me to her face.
Her nimble tongue, Love's lesser lightning, played
Within her mouth, and to my thoughts conveyed
　Swift orders that I should prepare to throw
　The all-dissolving thunderbolt below.
My fluttering soul, sprung with the pointed kiss,
Hangs hovering o'er her balmy brinks of bliss.
But whilst her busy hand would guide that part
Which should convey my soul up to her heart,
　In liquid raptures I dissolve all o'er,
　Melt into sperm, and spend at every pore.
A touch from any part of her had done't –
Her hand, her foot, her very look's a cunt.

Smiling, she chides in a kind murmuring noise
And from her body wipes the clammy joys,
When with a thousand kisses wandering o'er
My panting bosom, "Is there ten no more?"
She cries. "All this to love and rapture's due;
Must we not pay a debt to pleasure too?"

But I, the most forlorn, lost man alive
To show my wished obedience vainly strive.
I sigh, alas! and kiss – but cannot swive.
Eager desires confound my first intent,
Succeeding shame does more success prevent,
And rage at last confirms me impotent.
Ev'n her fair hand, which might bid heat return
To frozen age, and make cold hermits burn,
Applied to my dead cinder warms no more
Than fire to ashes could past flames restore.
Trembling, confusing, despairing, limber, dry,
A wishing, weak, unmoving lump I lie.

From "The Imperfect Enjoyment", John Wilmot,
Earl of Rochester (1647–1680)

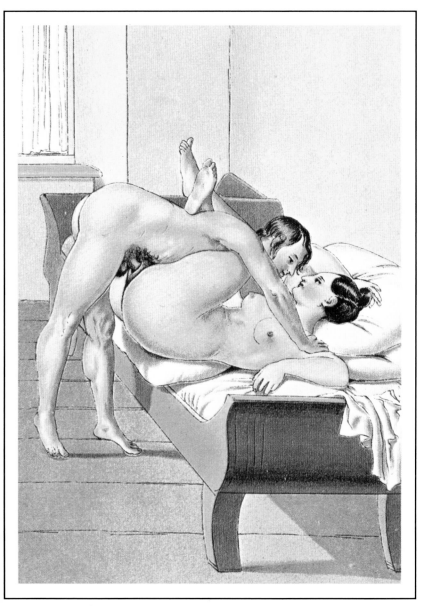

Peter Fendi (1796–1842)

D is for Diary

Lost Diary of the Marquis de Sade

James Maclean

Mislaid pages from the journal of Donatien-Alphonse, Marquis de Sade

In 1976, the 24-year-old Marquis de Sade, recently discharged from the army as a cavalry captain and married for little more than a year to Reneé Pélagic de Montreuil, leaves his young wife at the Normandy property of her parents for his ornamental cottage in the fashionable Parisian suburb of Arcueil. Banned for bad behaviour from most of the brothels of Paris and under surveillance by the police inspector Louis Marais, he leads the furtive existence of a clandestine libertine.

Arcueil, October 5, 1764

Aah…the relief of escaping from Echauffour! Even the name is claustrophobic. One more dinner party in the company of Madame de Montreuil would have induced insanity. Charming in small doses, maybe; witty on occasion, perhaps – and not at all bad-looking, it's true – but *au fond* – tough as old boots. She never draws breath and I suspect that behind that fragrant façade lurks the mother-in-law from hell. As I kissed my dear wife goodbye, her mother dropped a small bombshell: an old English friend of hers, the Countess of Stourpaine, might be coming to Paris and would I mind putting her up at Arcueil for a night or two? I had to agree without demur.

No time to lose. I want everything to be ready for my *grande partie de libertinage* next week. Wrote a note to Madame Brissault imploring her to send ten of her best girls for the evening despite what the wretched Marais has been telling her. And of course, ordered a good selection of whips, flails, martinets, and canes from Jobet in the rue Tire-Bourdain. Summoned Madame Charbonfaxe to see if she could come up with some sensible suggestions about the décor of my "special" room. I told the old embellisher that I needed something to suggest a whiff of brimstone at the same time as evoking the Grand Inquisitor's private torture chamber. "Ah," she twittered, "Monsieur would certainly be interested in our Basic Black damask range. I used it to great effect when I did up the Prince de Condé's *petite maison* down the road – he simply adores it!" Not entirely sure I wanted to turn de Condé into some sort of fashion leader, but told the old baggage to go ahead anyway.

Asked my man, La Grange, to take a carriage into town and find me four girls (at least) from the stage door of the *Comédi italienne* for tonight's fun. Now that the majority of Paris' brothels are closed to me, I have to rely on his fairly reasonable skills of procurement. But I like his choice – it's so refreshingly vulgar.

Arcueil, October 6. 1764

Last night's little entertainment – a trial run for the main event – was a success. All four girls soundly flogged. Sodomized two and took the others in the more usual manner but drank too much cognac. Got up at four o'clock to discover that Mme Charbonfaxe had sent in her decorators while I slept and, I have to admit, the room looks so sublimely grim that I became quite emotional and my eyes filled with tears. Found one of the *Comédi italienne* actresses asleep under the table and asked her if she would enjoy, for a further consideration, christening my new "chamber" with a sound whipping. "All right, give me the whip and take down your breeches," she said. Silly girl.

Arcueil, October 7, 1764

To my rage, Lady Stourpaine has arrived quite unexpectedly during one of our nightly rehearsals – just as I was about to deflower a young seamstress. As I showed my unwelcome guest to her room, a pair of naked nymphs flitted through the front hall hotly pursued by two priapic satyrs. To give her her due, this doughty matron did no more than snort loudly and raise one rather quizzical eyebrow. English sang-froid, no doubt. "We shall talk in the morning, Sir," she said, then added in an unpleasantly ominous tone of voice, "I always rise by seven and I shall doubtless see you then for *petit déjeuner.*" And hell will freeze over, Lady S, I thought to myself.

Arcueil, October 8, 1764

Perhaps the most unpleasant way I have ever been awoken is by the icy, foetid contents of a bidet breaking over my head at eight o'clock in the morning. Once I had recovered something approaching my normal composure, I noticed that a figure stood at the end of my bed, against the painfully strong light of an *open* window with *drawn* curtains and seemed to be saying something to me. For a moment I fancied this *contre-jour* apparition somewhat resembled an Avenging Angel. Of course, as a committed atheist I find all angels, and for that matter, God, laughable. Therefore, even though I was soaked, I laughed out loud. This was a mistake. I immediately received the remainder of the bidet's contents. As it departed through the door, I heard the apparition murmur, "I clearly remember that we arranged to meet for breakfast at seven o'clock, Sir. It is now eight. Pray be good enough to meet me downstairs at nine when I return from my morning ride."

Later

It is worse than I had supposed. Lady Stourpaine not only resembles the backside of an English mare and is prone to drenching her host in cold water, but she's also extremely obtuse. After giving me a short lecture on the virtues of early rising and the dangers of keeping dubious company, she could only talk of hunting foxes (at least you can eat *sanglier* – I mean, who's ever heard of *Renard à la bordelaise,* or *Renard à l'ancienne*?). This set me off on a rather brilliant (though I say it myself) gastro-philosophical discourse. At the end of it she remarked rather cryptically that that was all very well but that if God had wanted us to sit around thinking and spouting philosophy all day he would not have provided us with horses, hounds, and foxes. I fear she missed my point entirely. Thankfully she's spending the day with my mother-in-law in Paris, no doubt reporting on all the activities of last night.

Arcueil, October 10, 1764

Recently La Stourpaine and I have been following a policy of conspicuous avoidance, not always easy in a *cottage ornée.* In two days' time I will be playing host to the most sensational libertine event of the year and yet there is every indication that she will still be here to spy on me for my mother-in-law, despite the heaviest of hints that she has outstayed her welcome. Obviously, the only thing to do is to persuade her that the evening will be taken up by some amateur dramatics, that this would not be something to her liking, and that therefore she should retire early. As insurance I will get La Grange to slip a sleeping draught into her hot cocoa.

Later

The conversation went something like this:

"Madame, I will be entertaining a small group of friends on Thursday to take part in some amateur theatricals."

"How delightful, Sir! I look forward to being most entertained."

"I fear that you will only find them tedious, Madame."

"*Au contraire, Monsieur*. I am not averse to theatre. My late husband and I much enjoyed Mr Garrick's performances of Hamlet and King Lear at Drury Lane."

Arcueil, October 12, 1764

The great day has arrived! Let us hope that it will not be entirely ruined by La Stourpaine's presence. The consecrated hosts have failed to appear, which has also put a slight dampener on things. No black mass is complete without them. Never mind, we shall extemporize.

Arcueil, October 13, 1764

To begin with, everything went beautifully. La Grange assured me that Lady Stourpaine had drained her drugged chocolate at a gulp and was now snoring heavily in her bedroom. By ten o'clock I had deflowered two virgins, sodomized six girls and four boys, whipped and flogged and beaten just about everybody, performed several exquisite blasphemies, and, of course, had philosophized to a rapt audience between the bouts of physical activity. My energies were beginning to flag. It was my turn for a dose of the Spanish Fly that La Grange had passed around to enliven the proceedings. Just as I was about to mix some into my cognac, I noticed that everybody had fallen asleep, albeit the men with enormous erections. It didn't take a genius (such as myself) to deduce that my valet had somehow contrived to mix the sleeping draught with my best ground Cantharides.

As I wondered what to do next, Lady Stourpaine, naked and dishevelled, ran into the room. I managed to conceal myself from this terrifying old harridan and observed her discreetly from behind a column as she fell upon La Grange's somnolent form, impaling herself on his massive member with some strange English hunting cry and started to ride him as if she were pursuing the fox. Only seconds later there was a fine commotion outside and then the sound of heavy footsteps on the stairs. From my place of concealment I saw the doors flung open by liveried servants and the immaculate figure of my mother-in-law appear. A deliciously awkward pause ensued and for the first time in her life my mother-in-law seemed at a loss for words. For the first time in *my* life, I allowed discretion to be the better part of valour and quietly withdrew to another room so that the two old friends might enjoy a more private encounter.

This short story first appeared in The Erotic Review *(see page 319).*

"*E*" is another outstanding, thrusting letter with its three-pronged approach as a capital and a single, upstanding probe in its lower case form — an apt character then for Erection, leading, we hope, to Ejaculation. Either way, "*E*" is an Exhibitionist.

Erection

And what a glorious sight it is! But ways of successful stimulation, as with women's genitalia, vary according to the individual and stage of arousal – the more advanced usually benefiting from a surprisingly vigorous approach. Sensations around the glans are especially variable. The frenulum, the fold of tissue linking the glans to the main body of the shaft, can be either a source of ecstasy or squirmingly painful to the touch. The coronal ridge around the head of the penis is another area of high sensitivity that requires careful exploration. But the perineum – the area between the penis root and the anus – is the winner. Knead it firmly with one hand while working the penis with the other, and don't neglect the balls.

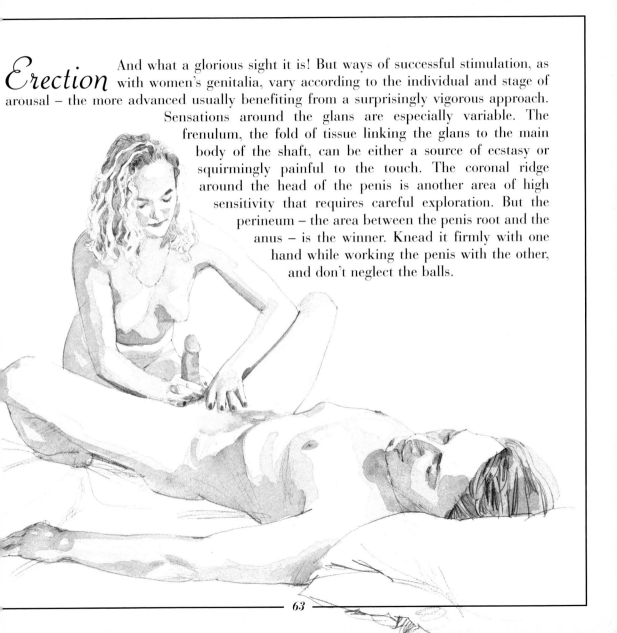

EMS No one can accuse us of not being inventive when it comes to sex – as a species, at least. And so we find folk recognizing the potential for sexual pleasure in what would seem the most unlikely quarters and under unprepossessing circumstances. For instance, there we are, in dire need of back pain relief or desperate to lose weight, but that's all forgotten when we discover an alternative, recreational use for our TENS (Transdermal Electric Neural Stimulator) machine and our Slendatone or Electrical Muscular Stimulation (EMS) device. But misappropriation of these electrical gadgets is not to be recommended in the interests of safety, and in any case, there are easier ways. Devices are now available that are specifically designed for sexual purposes, namely Electro-Stimulation Boxes (battery or mains-operated), complete with a variety of toys to play with – cock rings, butt plugs, etc. A serious note of warning: these machines should never be used above the waist because of risk to the heart, and all safety warnings issued by the manufacturers must be carefully heeded.

Endytophilia This may be an unusual term, denoting those who would rather have sex with someone clothed than naked, but it is a common enough desire. At the extreme end, it may indicate full-blown fetishism, particularly if there is an attendant demand for certain kinds of clothing to be worn, such as all black or the tell-tale latex or leather. On a less specialist level, the tantalizing glimpse of "forbidden" flesh is evocative of those first furtive fumblings of adolescence. These being such a formative part of our sexual lives, we may feel a subliminal longing to recapture them, thus re-engaging with the raw intensity of our early sexual sensations. There is also something inherently erotic in juxtaposition and contrast – the smooth, synthetic encasement of stocking ending abruptly in a mass of soft, yielding thigh; the contrast in texture of fabric and wiry pubes. And finally, of course, there is the element of spontaneity and urgency, wrenching down trousers, lifting skirts, and merely pulling underwear aside to facilitate copulation.

Exhibitionism

An exhibitionist is someone who gains sexual excitement from exposing their "private parts" to others. This may immediately conjure up that ubiquitous, opportunist haunter of public places – the raincoat-sporting park flasher, or the slightly more sophisticated magazine masturbator of train fame. However, exhibitionism is much more likely to be in your face in the form of mainstream women's fashion. So there are many different degrees and manifestations of the sport. We may, for instance, get a thrill out of the thought of a passer-by on the street catching sight of us through the window in a state of undress. Or maybe we might take our exhibitionist inspiration from that most memorable cinematic moment, when Sharon Stone uncrosses her legs in *Basic Instinct*. A more advanced, consensual form would be having sex publicly in a swingers or sex club, and some offer special rooms for participants to be viewed, thus catering for exhibitionists and voyeurs at the same time. Anticipation of exhibitionist opportunities can be very much part of the turn-on.

Sylvie Jones (Contemporary)

Exhibitionism ...

Eric Wilkins (Contemporary)

Sweet Disorder

A sweet disorder in the dress
Kindles in clothes a wantonness:
A lawn about the shoulders thrown
Into a fine distraction,
An **erring lace**, which here and there
Enthrals the crimson stomacher,
A cuff neglectful, and thereby
Ribbands to flow confusedly,
A winning wave, deserving note,
In the tempestuous petticoat,
A careless shoe-string, in whose tie
I see a wild civility –
Do more bewitch me than when art
Is too precise in every part.

Robert Herrick (1591–1674)

Peter Fendi (1796–1842)

E is for Extra-Marital Sex

The Restaurant

Justine Dubois

Weeping words fuel his passion. A hand touches him lightly. His tongue murmurs assent. He awakes from his dream to find her cupped close to him. Her skin is warm and perfumed. His body rises and falls in gently inquiry, as yet unsure. Is she beautiful? He does remember her name. She does not yet, turning his arms to look at him. With soft whimperings her body spells gentle accord. Is she gentle? He cannot remember the night.

Her arpeggio scent melds with their own secret perfume. It is like a shared breath between them. Her shoulder is lean and finely drawn. A blush of warmth settles on her skin. He only remembers rejection. His body begins to respond. His arms draw her closer to him. His mouth softly sweeps away the dark blonde tresses trapped beneath her necklace. The rasp of his unshaven chin grazes the pale flesh of her upper back. His hand and wrist are like fine architecture. He reaches to caress her soft round breasts, delicately assessing their weight, arousing their nipples, as strident as heaven. He cannot remember. His left hand rests briefly on her upper thigh, his fingers interlocking with hers. He strokes and separates her round buttocks, readjusting them to his lap. The girl arches her back in acquiescence. With every new nuance of movement her secret perfume injects the air, creating a bower between them. He touches his penis in reassurance, teasing at his own flesh with knowing caresses. He makes of his hand a brush of pleasure. He can feel her moistness, upturned in his lap.

Only as he enters her does he start to remember her a little. There is a moment of stillness, almost a sense of surprise, before he invents a rhythm. Still she does not turn to look at him. His pace is deliberate and hard-hitting. He feels heavy within her. She stretches against him, lengthening her legs until she stands tiptoe on his instep. Now, finely balanced, it is she who has control. She dances upon him, evoking a faster pace. He groans in sweet delight. He remembers the woman from last night, her face distorted by anger. He recalls the dark mole on her neck intriguingly juxtaposed with the dancing drop of her earring. The girl in his arms murmurs her excitement. Again, he resumes charge, this time pursuing his massive energies deep within her. She calls out in delicious aching pain as he touches her womb. With one hand he grasps the side of her hips, with the other the small of her back, directing her, directing them both; the momentary silences of heaven.

He half-remembers the restaurant where he ate last night, its Japanese motif of sliding screen walls divided into squares of clouded glass, remembers his hors d'oeuvre of crab with lemon grass and thyme, remembers the glass of St Emilion thrown in his face, the ruination of his shirt and tie. But something else hovers at the very edge of his memory: a woman's face, exquisitely beautiful. The girl in his arms tires momentarily, no longer following their rhythm, rag doll.

Briefly, he ignores her, pursuing his angry thoughts and sensations to completion. But graciousness forbids. He allows her to come to rest, lapsing into his lap. Neither of them speaks, except in the murmurous language of lovers. He can feel her heart beating beneath her breasts; he can feel their weight, their roundness – it is a joy to him. The perfume they share is now like a room in which they might both forever live, profound and all consuming. He slips from her, shifting, to rest his back against hers. Tiredness deserts her. She is immediately alert, and bereft. With the dark blonde muzz of her hair still concealing her face, she crouches, turning towards him. He witnesses her narrow waist, the pretty length and roundness of her breasts as she raises herself into kneeling position beside him. Her scent excites him. Why was that woman so menacingly angry with him in the restaurant last night? Beneath her curtain of hair, he now sees the girl's mouth. He catches sight of its exquisite curves: the rounded edges of its upper lip, perfectly indented beneath the square tip of her nose, as sharply defined as good drawing; the generous *moue* of its lower lip which seems, by comparison, dissolved and imprecise, like a soft kiss left glancing on warm skin, a stain of beauty.

Mesmerized, he watches as this precise, beautiful shape descends upon him, witnesses it stretch to a distorted silent scream as she first nestles and then lifts to her soft, welcome mouth the bruised beautiful head of his penis, as sculptural and heavy as a column. He watches her engulf him up and down in a long-necked swallow, watches himself re-emerge tall and proud, to be conjured into even fiercer response by the cunning whip of his foreskin. No sense of responsibility fractures his desire. He recalls the woman in the restaurant saying that he was louche, that he had no pride, that he no longer made love to her. Her mouth, too, had been contorted into a silent scream, a scream of loud loathing. As she crouches by his thigh, the girl's necklace, a heavy gold chain, trails against the length of his penis. He whispers his

pleasure and surprise. He is close, so very close. He can remember the woman's abuse more precisely now. She had been wearing red, a colour he had never seen her in before. She had aimed something at his head, something heavy, an ashtray maybe? It had struck the side of his temple. He had lost consciousness. He remembers the stroke of the ambulance, its siren. But why? He and his ex-wife had not lived together for more than a year. The girl in his lap senses his excitement. Still kneeling, she straddles him, riding towards his knees, the hourglass slenderness of her waist and hips revealed. As she half turns, he can just see the profile of her face. It is a face of bright joy, of delicate definition, a face of exquisite beauty. Never before.

He feels, as if for the first time, the fierce, close drag of her flesh upon his. His pleasure is mounting. He leans her gently back against him. With the soft tip pads of his long elegant fingers he caresses her. She calls out in rapture, her body racked by a new independent rhythm that repeats and repeats itself and then subsides, her blonde head sweet-comforting in the recesses of his neck. It feels as though they might have known each other forever. He remembers the Italian waiter from last night wringing his hands and murmuring "Peccato, che peccato" under his breath, as he and his ex-wife exchanged insults. He remembers someone trying to gently mop at his stained shirt and tie, and then tucking a piece of paper into his breast pocket. He recalls the frightened look on his ex-wife's face as she was escorted from the restaurant, violent with anger and abuse. Was it the waiter who had called the police? The girl raises herself from his lap and, as she does so, he too kneels, encouraging her face downwards into a pillow. He enters her from behind. She sweet-moans her approval. He strokes the long splendour of her back downwards, flattening her upper body like a cat as she arches herself towards him in welcome. Again he moves within her, with complete authority now. Her skin has become his skin. His hand upon her has become pure knowledge. He races at her, almost cruelly now. She calls out. But he does not desist. This is his moment. He will not be cheated of its ecstasy. The rhythm between them is painful, fierce, almost dangerous. And then, at the point of her most exquisite anguish, he too calls out, an incoherent fluttering sound, and falls against her, juddering, in soft, sweet acknowledgement of pleasure.

He folds her, without seeing, in his arms, her head against his chest. For a minute or two he sleeps, and then opens his eyes to look at her. She looks up at him, unashamed, her blue eyes wide open and truthful.

And suddenly he remembers their sweet darling of a waitress, with her bob of dark blonde hair, remembers her perfume and the clever shape of her beautiful mouth, remembers her tucking something into his breast pocket as he lay waiting for the ambulance on the restaurant floor. And he also recalls his wife's almost psychopathic fury as he casually confessed, "I don't think I have ever seen a woman more instantaneously beautiful and desirable than our delicious delight of a waitress". A barometer of anguish had swept through her features. "I was about to tell you that I missed you."

This short story first appeared in The Erotic Review *(see page 319).*

You can't help but purse your lips to issue the soft-edged but firm-centred "F". And that delicious interplay of hard and soft we see exploited in Fellatio, Fantasy, and Fetishism. This is the pinup of the erotic alphabet, bringing us that wonderfully full-frontal term for the sacred sex act itself — Fuck.

Fellatio

Giving head, polishing the knob, playing the pink oboe, nose to hose…there are as many variations on the practice as there are names for it, so there's no risk of anyone getting bored. However, she might get jaw-ache, which is one of the reasons why orchestrating the performance is a good idea – for her as well as him. This is when you can explore those extra-sensitive areas of the glans and the coronal ridge with much less fear of being heavy-handed (mask those fangs!), provided, of course, that you can produce, and keep on producing, enough saliva for lubrication. Seek out with your tongue the triangular-shaped ridge of tissue, the frenulum, at the back of the glans.

Faking It Ever since the show-stopping fake orgasm scene in the movie *When Harry Met Sally*, we've all felt better and worse about it. On the one hand, the concept has been released into the communal psyche and therefore we are forced to engage with it, which has to be beneficial if there is a real problem that needs attending to. On the other hand, we are plagued from time to time by fears that we don't and won't know who is faking what and when. If you're going through a really bad period of self-doubt, you might even believe that you're faking gratification to yourself! But there are times when it's just the polite, only decent thing to do – when you've lured someone to bed, for instance, and suddenly found that you've lost your sexual appetite; or you're too tired or hungover to make a decent fist of it. For men, of course, faking is a greater challenge – how do you fake an erection? However, if the erection is achievable but the orgasm elusive, a condom is a useful aid to concealing the giveaway absence of semen.

Fanny Hill John Cleland (1709–1789) was the English author of *Memoirs of a Woman of Pleasure*, commonly known as *Fanny Hill*, often regarded as the first acclaimed pornographic work in English. In the form of letters from the spirited heroine to an unknown female confidante, Fanny describes her scandalously successful rise through the ranks of society as a prostitute and her sexual encounters along the way in graphic detail. As much as its explicit content, it was shocking as a critique of the establishment and its attitudes from the mouth of such a disreputable figure, and parodied the moralism of the likes of Daniel Defoe. For his trouble, Cleland was tried for obscenity – despite the fact that the book was a bestseller – but managed to escape punishment with the plea that he had written it only for the money. The publication was still managing to cause affront in the 1960s, when the first unabridged version was published in the UK and subsequently confiscated by the law. At the same time, in the US the Massachusetts Supreme Court declared the book obscene.

Fantasy This used to be something of a dirty word, synonymous with an exclusively male preserve, where men mechanistically wanked over crude, exploitative pornographic magazines or videos. Thankfully, times and attitudes have moved on and fantasy can now assume its rightful, crucial role in ensuring our sexual health and happiness. We can draw on the wealth of source material now freely available, both in word and imagery, to feed and inspire our imaginations. But it's within our individual minds that the real creative process takes place, and the potential for home-grown fantasy is as abundant as our minds are fertile. Once hatched and honed, a favourite fantasy scenario can be instantly invoked to trigger arousal or hasten or heighten orgasm. Some people need to keep fantasies private in order to preserve their potency; for others, much of the thrill will come from externalizing the fantasy, either talking about it or enacting it with a "symbolic" use of props or items of clothing. Most fantasies are specifically not designed to be turned into actuality because in reality they would be undesirable, for instance being raped – a common fantasy.

Fetishism A fetish originally denoted, and still does in one sense, a talisman – an object with magical protective powers. This meaning is perhaps not so far removed from the more familiar sense – a specific object on which a person is dependent for their sexual pleasure to a varying degree, ultimately constituting a substitute for a sexual partner. For a fetishist, the fetish is his or her good-luck charm, a potent symbol of sexual success that protects against the fears that direct sexual expression may hold. The range of fetish objects is standard and can be divided into two categories: clothing (boots and shoes, underwear, hats, gloves) and materials (leather, latex, rubber, fur). Interestingly, though, fashions do seem to come and go in fetishism, with fur and silk being supplanted these days by the harder-hitting leather and rubber. But that's not the whole fetish picture. A parallel field of fetishism is known as "partial", where the chosen object of desire is a part of the body – breasts, foot, neck, hair.

Let's **Fuck**, Dear Heart

Let's fuck, dear heart, let's have it in and out,
For we're obliged to fuck for being born,
And as I crave for cunt, you ache for horn,
Because the world would not make sense without.

If after death it were decent to be had,
I'd say: Let's fuck, let's fuck so much we die;
There we'll all fuck – you Adam, Eve and I –
For they invented death and thought it bad.

Really it's true that if those first two thieves
Had never eaten that perfidious fruit,
We'd still know how to fuck (though not wear leaves).

But no more gossip now; let's aim and shoot
The prick right to the heart, and make the soul
Burst as it dies in concert with the root.

And could your generous hole
Take in as witness these bobbing buoys
For inside testimony of our joys?

Pietro Aretino (1492–1556)

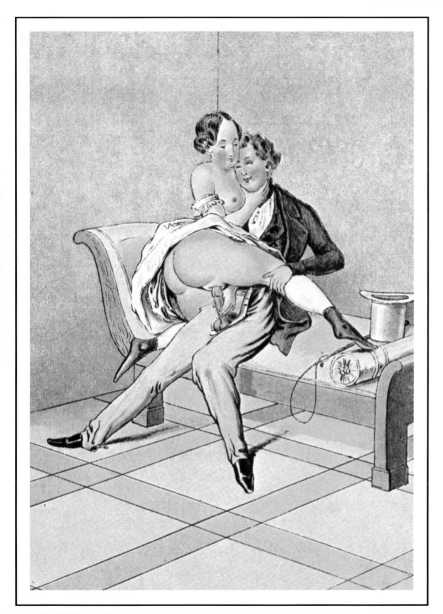

Peter Fendi (1796–1842)

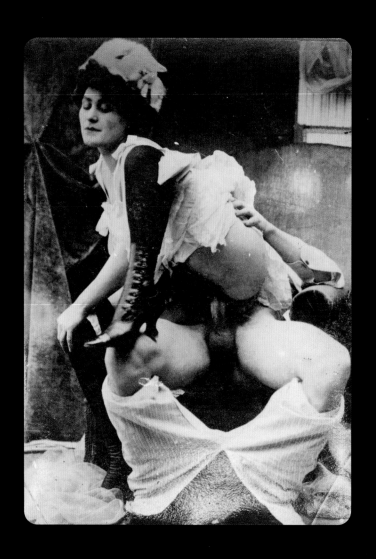

Anon. (19th Century)

F is for Fantasy

Fantasy & Fear

Justine Dubois

They share an early supper. She dresses demurely, in black. He arrives straight from work, pinstriped. The restaurant is just a few streets away; a boisterous, fashionable corridor running between the pavement and its own kitchen. On either side, men bowed down by the self-importance of work succeed in looking both bored and animated. Next to them sit women, disdainfully pretty in floral chic. The waiter brings them a menu.

She is translucent-skinned and youthful, her auburn hair a confection of unruly curls. Opposite her, the Prussian blue of his shirt matches his eyes. He is straight-backed and aquiline, with single plumes of grey at his forehead. He is charmingly unaware of his own good looks.

The waiter brings them pasta, steeped in squid ink. Around them, the restaurant is a hubbub of animation, but their concentration on each other is far greater. They are like fierce lovers in a Watteau landscape. Everyone else is at play; only they are serious. Their love makes no attempt to exclude, and yet always succeeds effortlessly in so doing. Slowly, the room begins to revolve around their passion. Covert glances, part-envy, part-amazement, stalk them. Yet they only see each other. They talk keenly, their faces alight with delicious smiles. They share a dish of strawberries decorated with mint, white-veiled in sugar. He pays the bill and then orders himself an extra coffee. "Are you having something more to drink?" he asks.

"No, nothing, thank you. I am leaving." She stands up.

"Won't they think you are deserting me?"

"I expect you can bear the ignominy of it," she teases. A moment of panic.

"But I assumed..." She smiles and makes to walk out. "There is something I need to do, a surprise. Join me in ten minutes if you like."

At home, she climbs the stairs. She throws her keys on to the bed, then removes her top layer of clothing; the anonymous polo-neck, the dark skirt.

She exchanges her mid-height heels for something more precipitous. She only retains her emerald and gold earrings, which dazzle in her reddish hair.

Beneath the banality of her outer garments, she is no longer anonymous. At her waist is a suspender belt of black, beribboned satin, its suspenders dragged low over the long, smooth-stockinged curve of her thighs. Her figure is round, shapely. The bra she wears is like a hieroglyph, a signal of support, but curiously ineffectual. Her breasts tumble from its constraining architecture like ripe fruit. A red rosebud sits coyly at the centre of its divisive under-bridge. As if to make up for its faulty design, its bra straps are broad and fat with expensive black lace, the same quipure lace that fails to veil her nipples. She checks her watch; only a few minutes to go. She twists her hair into a chignon and secures it with a black velvet ribbon-bow, attached to a silver clip. He always likes to see the swan length of her slender neck.

She is rushing now. She searches, last minute, in a drawer, her supple body jackknifing gracefully on her vertiginous heels. She finds what she is looking for, a mask, a plain sleeper's mask; no feathers, no allusive cat features to enhance its design, simply a pragmatic mask, with which to cut out light and sight. As she stands up, she remembers her panties, black butterflies flocked on to filmy chiffon. She steps from them and they curl on the carpet, like a hairnet. The cat pounces on them, ready to play. The ten minutes are up. She dashes to the front door and opens it, leaving it slightly ajar. She then returns to the subdued lighting of the sitting-room and, with one last-minute glance at herself in the mirror, fastens the mask over her eyes. She then positions herself on the sofa, arms stretched outwards along its high back, her legs spread invitingly wide.

She waits. The minutes pass intensely. She experiences a moment of sharp *frisson*. The front door is open. Anyone can enter. She feels blind, vulnerable, exposed. Seconds of darkness feel like an eternity of waiting. Fantasy and fear invade her every sense. Her hearing grows unusually acute. She finds herself interpreting every stray noise. No one arrives. She hears the creek of a distant floorboard, followed by the shrill of a siren from the street. Again silence. Her fear mounts tantalizingly. She feels a sudden draught of cold air. No sound. She is stranded in darkness. There are slight echoes of movement. By now, she is keyed-up, her feelings polarized, both confident and afraid. She struggles to maintain her composure. From beneath her mask slip involuntary smiles. His tongue, as it is placed full against her, feels like a sable brush, plump with pigment. It is the most delicious sensation. No one speaks. He is familiar, and yet not completely so. The doubt is exciting. All her senses are alert to every nuance of his touch.

He uses his mouth like an instrument. His hands have not yet touched her, simply the clever explorations of his fat tongue. The cage of her hips rises to greet him in silence. His tongue washes over her and then seeks out her mouth. The muzzle of his face is wet against hers. She can taste herself in the *longueur* of his kisses.

Now, at last, his hands are upon her. He touches her nipples, as they tumble from their confining lace, and murmurs his approval. He drags her low in the lap of the sofa, her buttocks arched forward. She feels his penis brush against the warmth of her thighs as he enters her. And now, almost familiar, the sense of him within her. But still a hint of surprise. His energies blend with hers, bounce within her.

He turns her round, cupping her breasts to enter her from behind. He is about to lose control. He withdraws. Blindfolded, silent still, he leads her upstairs, feet faltering, carefully negotiating her way. She is disorientated. Her feet stumble on the stairs. She stands still, listening, whilst he opens various doors. She is perplexed. He leads her forward. He stretches her out on the bed, lengthening his frame over hers. He feels capable, strong. He kisses her ardently. Her perfume has become an amalgam of scents. She raises the cat's cradle of her hips in welcome; sweet familiarity. Then, something new, he bites her neck. Together they race incoherently. He leans back, kneeling between her legs to kiss her. She is close, so very close. Sensations of sweetness envelop her. Her body speeds to voracious silence. She calls out. He clasps her briefly, subsiding in his arms.

And then, still wrapped in darkness, she mounts him, riding him as he had previously ridden her. They fit together well. She can feel the draw of his flesh on hers. She clasps to his midriff like a buckle. They lose momentum, briefly. To alter the rhythm, she sits up tall, breasts bouncing. Beneath her mask, she smiles gladly and stretches her hand behind her to caress him lightly. It is the extra touch-paper of ignition. The sound of footsteps on the stairs. They had forgotten to close the front door. His body races in a fit of pleasure and submission. Her features are suffused with happy warmth. She makes to discard her mask triumphantly.

Her husband's voice calls, "Sorry to have kept you, darling…An old friend of mine arrived at the restaurant just as I was leaving. It would have been rude not to talk…" She turns in desperation towards the door. Her happiness becomes distress.

Behind her stands her husband, surveying the baroque carnage of her lovemaking. As he does so, the blonde, handsome stranger rises from their bed.

This short story first appeared in The Erotic Review *(see page 319).*

"*G*" is a defining character when it comes to matters sexual, pinpointing that mythical, elusive Holy Grail of enrapture — the *G*-spot. It also helps to describe that traditional saucy sex snare (now reconstituted as a cure for *VPL*), the *G*-string. Rather less respectable under this letter we offer you Group sex and Golden showers.

Group Sex

If we haven't had the chance (or the nerve) to sample it, most of us have undoubtedly fantasized about it. The risks are, of course, as obvious as the attractions. Depicted here is perhaps the least emotionally threatening option – having sex with your own partner in sight of another couple. The daring of breaking the privacy taboo, the element of exhibitionism and the giving over of oneself to wanton sex is an intoxicatingly erotic mix. But could you do it in practice? If not, it's still great as a fantasy!

Geisha

There is something enduringly erotic about geisha. First there is their artificial, doll-like, iconic garb – surely a fetishist's dream. Then there is the whole notion of offering up oneself utterly to their gracious, elaborate entertainment, rich in skill and ritual, whether it's performing the tea ceremony, dancing and singing, or playing that most challenging of instruments, the three-stringed shamisen. This weighty delivery is then deliciously tempered by their delicately orchestrated teasing and flirtatiousness. The whole tradition is then cloaked in mystery and wonder, with the underlying *frisson* of self-sacrifice and pain – all those stories of training for years from an early age, holding their hands in buckets of iced water, and practising the shamisen in the freezing cold until their fingers bleed. But most of all, the geisha's enigmatic appeal comes down to the ultimate question in everyone's minds: do they do it or don't they? With all the rest on offer, it's doubtful whether they would need to in any case.

Glory Holes

Again, we see man at his most inventive and opportunist best in this phenomenon. An army of randy handymen have been slaving away, drilling holes in each wall of every stall in the men's rooms of many nations to accommodate any passing "stiffy" in need of oral attention. One hopes these guys were careful to judge the height of these ingenious orifices, otherwise the experience could be a most uncomfortable and frustrating one, although it would undoubtedly cause problems for those of abnormal proportions in any dimension. Some adult bookstores also helpfully provide this facility in the partitions of booths for watching videos in private – it's certainly a sight more satisfying than popcorn. This "hole-in-the-wall" style of sex may appear brutally impersonal to some, but it does allow the participants to maintain their anonymity. For others the idea of having passing sexual contact with a stranger will be central to the pleasure to be had from the experience.

Golden Showers This practice is now more commonly included under the blanket term "watersports" and picturesquely describes the act of urinating over a sexual partner, or being urinated on. By all accounts, this seems to have caught on of late, and usually involves the woman urinating over the man in the bath, often in a standing position, which, as a peeing stance, in itself offers novelty value for her. Favourite areas for showering are the face and mouth, genitals, buttocks, and breasts. Care must be taken that urine doesn't enter the mouth, anus, or vagina since it can contain viruses or bacteria. The psychology here may be one of power for her, at the same time as indulging in the thrill of "unacceptable" behaviour. For him there may be the reciprocal turn-on of powerlessness and abuse, and in general there is a base, animalistic tenor to the proceedings, which always has its liberating attractions. But peeing can also play a part in solo sex. The same feelings of breaking a taboo can combine with the pure sensation of urine seeping out and trickling down the leg, if you're a woman and standing, or peeing in your underwear in a brief return to the freedom of infancy.

G-Spot German gynaecologist Ernst Grafenberg first staked a claim to this mysterious little love button way back in 1950, even giving it his name – the Grafenberg Spot, now affectionately known as the G-spot. It remained in obscurity until it was relaunched in the early 1980s by the researchers Perry and Whipple in their book *The G-Spot and Other Recent Discoveries About Human Sexuality*. Not content with just stirring the sexual stew on that point, they threw in the concept of female ejaculation to spice things up. Since then the G-spot has had its ups and downs in its aspirations as the ultimate fount of orgasmic gratification, and even in relatively recent times it has been dismissed as a fallacy. Currently, more credence has been given to the view that the entire anterior wall of the vagina, rather than just one single spot, is highly sensitive. If you're still on the trail, it usually lies about 3 cm (1.2 in) into the vagina, directly behind the pubic bone.

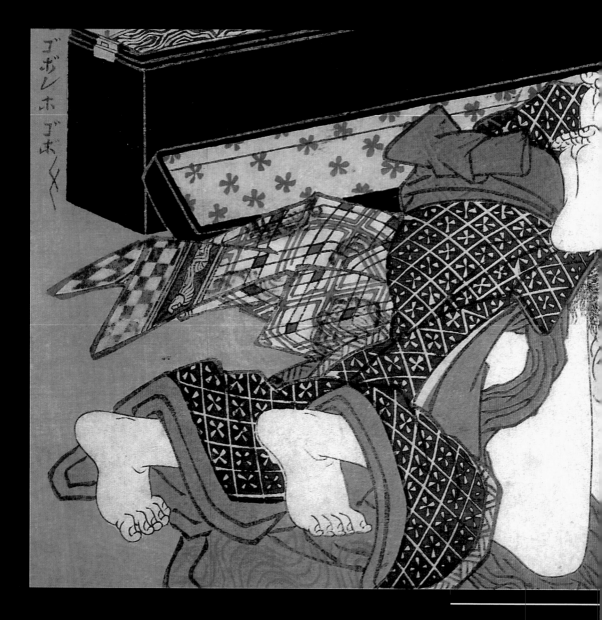

The *Game* of Cards

As I was a-walking one midsummer's morning
I heard the birds whistle and the nightingales play
And there did I spy a beautiful maiden
As I was a-walking all on the highway

O where are you going, my fair pretty lady?
O where are you going so early this morn?
She said: I'm going down to visit my neighbours
I'm going down to Leicester, the place I was born

It's: May I come with you, my sweet pretty darling?
May I go along in your sweet compan-ie?
Then she turned her head and smiling all at me
Saying: You may come with me, kind sir, if you please

We hadn't been walking but a few miles together
Before this young damsel began to show free
She sat herself down, saying: Sit down beside me
And the games we shall play shall be one, two, and three

I said: My dear lady, if you're fond of the gaming
There's one **game** I know I would like you to learn
The game it is called: The Game of All Fours
So I took out my pack and began the first turn

She cut the cards first and I fell a-dealing
I dealt her a trump and myself the poor jack
She led off her ace and stole my jack from me
Saying: Jack is the card I like best in your pack

Since I dealt them last time, it's your turn to shuffle
And my turn to show the best card in the pack
Once more she'd the ace and the deuce for to beat me
Once again I had lost when I laid down poor jack

So I took up my hat and I bid her: Good morning
I said: You're the best that I know at this game
She answered: Young man, if you'll come back tomorrow
We'll play the game over and over again

Traditional song

94

Fair Game, Thomas Rowlandson (1756–1827)

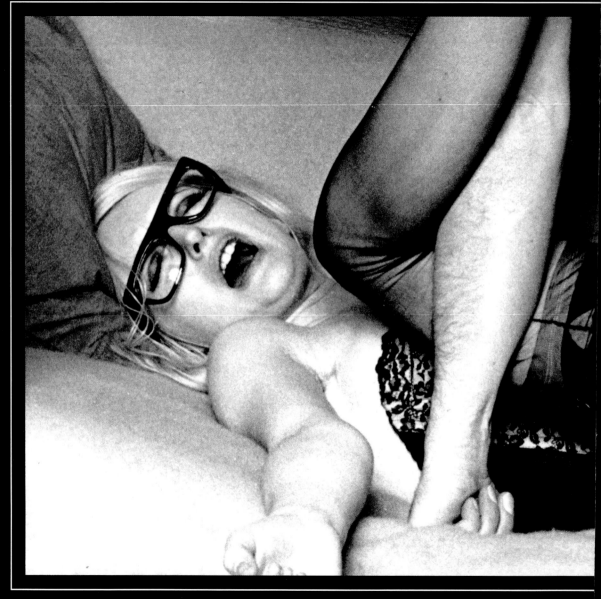

Eric Wilkins (Contemporary)

Finding the G-spot ...

G is for Group Sex

Claude's Story

Breton/Tauzin

from *The Devil's Whisper*. The Erotic Print Society

We slept. I was woken by Birgit's hand between my legs, searching for my spent cock.

Birgit wanted to be fucked again, very badly, I thought, and I was not yet ready. The Devil

whispered something in my ear and I passed it on to Birgit in a low, urgent voice. Her reaction

was to shudder, I thought from disgust, but she said "Yes!" in a low, passionate tone.

I took her firmly by the arm, made her get up, and walked her over to the little balcony outside the window. We looked down into the street below and saw no one suitable. Eventually a couple of sailor boys strolled into view. I knew that if they looked up they would be able to see Birgit's breasts and my naked chest. They looked slightly drunk, but they were at the happy stage of drunkenness. To my surprise, it was Birgit who called down to them, "Want some free pussy? Come up here, boys…" and then she looked at me and laughed. The sailors glanced up, puzzled, until they located the source of this delightful invitation, then grinned and ran for the entrance below. I felt her wriggle, as if she had suddenly had a change of heart, but I took her face in my hands and I spat at her, "Do you want more cock or not? Make up your mind!" She sighed and I felt her body slump against me in a gesture of mute resignation. We both knew that she did.

There were footsteps on the bare boards of the staircase outside the apartment and the sailors were soon knocking on Birgit's door. I met them in the little vestibule.

"Look – help me out here, boys," I said in a low voice that I hoped Birgit wouldn't hear, "I've just fucked my girl and she's still desperate for more cock – but I'm totally fucked-out!"

The two shipmates looked at me suspiciously, then at each other, as if there were a catch to this otherwise splendid suggestion. But they could see Birgit standing behind me naked, legs well apart; they could see the dribble of semen running from the pink and bruised lips of Birgit's cunt and Sailor A, dark and swarthy with curly hair, said, "OK, we'll fuck her for you Mister. No problem!" And they started to pull off their uniforms, their squashed hats with red pompoms sailing through the air to land in a corner. I put an arm around Birgit and realized that she was shivering, as if she had a fever. "Are you nervous?" I asked. "Do you want to change your mind?" She looked up at me, her eyes half-closed and she smiled at me as if I were a simpleton. I realized that she was literally shaking with lust, trembling with lust and excitement, so I pushed her back down on to the bed and parted her thighs so that her cunt was accessible to us. I stood back and realized how beautiful and powerful she was as she lay there, passive, open to the world, yet with all of us in her thrall. Sailor B, with red hair and freckles, asked, "Does she take it up the arse?" At first I was a little cross: he was acting as if Birgit simply wasn't there, as if this had nothing to do with her. So I said, a little curtly, "Why don't you ask her yourself. Her name is Birgit, by the way."

But by then, Sailor A was standing over Birgit; he already had his cock in her mouth, and she was gorging on it, as if it were some incredible, irresistible delicacy that she had to stuff as much of into her mouth as she could, squeezing his balls in time to the lunges she made with her mouth. Sailor B was sitting next to her, his erection at the perpendicular and was pawing her superb breasts, rolling the swollen, red nipples between finger and thumb.

I sat the other side of her and whispered to her, "I think they'll want to fuck you in the cunt and arse at the same time. Have you ever done that? Would you like to do that – a sandwich? Just think... those two big cocks inside you at once! Incredible. I'd love to watch that... and maybe I'd fuck you after." She whimpered softly with desire. My hand wandered down to the matted nest of hair below her belly. I parted the strands and found her juicy slit. There was still more juice now, a fresh supply... she was ready again. She was ready to fuck. Answering the three of us at once, she looked up and smiled a mad little smile – half apologetic and half hysterical – "Yes... I want you all inside me at once." Straight away, Birgit got up and pushed back the sailor sitting, Sailor B, and with a rather uncustomary awkwardness, gingerly lowered herself down on to his upright cock, still facing her audience of two.

It was somehow a magnificent, moving sight, and I soon realized why she was being so careful – she was about to take the full, quivering spear of flesh up her arse. She steadied herself with one hand on his big muscular thigh while with the other she delicately circled his cock with her fingers and swept its head along the length of her dripping cunt. Thus suitably smeared with her vagina's oily secretions, she shifted the head into the slight declivity of her arsehole and, frowning with concentration, started to lower herself. As Birgit slowly impaled herself in a way that she had never attempted before, Sailor A knelt between her thighs and started to lick at her swollen and oozing pussy.

I stood a little to one side and caught her eye, trying to read in her expression what was going on, trying to make sense of what was happening between us. It was as if the two men were automatons that I had introduced for her exclusive pleasure, to assuage her nymphomaniac desires, but both of us knew that this was really for my entertainment as much as hers, and I could feel my cock hardening once more. All this was communicated in the gaze between us, in the slight, fleeting, grimaces of pain that she made as her anus and rectum adjusted to this new and extraordinary intrusion. Then she started to rise and fall on Sailor B's cock, slowly at first, then faster and faster until she reached a steady rhythm that seemed to suit her. Even as he bounced up and down on his cock, breasts dancing wildly, even in this slightly absurd and vulnerable position, she held my gaze and her cool grey eyes locked on mine. I became acutely aware of every new and subtle transformation in the map of her face. Soon I detected the ghost of a smile, a proud smile with just a hint of a raised eyebrow… now I saw the twitch of her mouth's corner and finally, there it was, a broad, jubilant grin which said everything.

It told me that – if she ever had been – she was no longer particularly upset about our parting. It told me that I had been a fool to take her so much for granted, and never to guess that there was an exciting, sexual woman beneath her *gemütlich* exterior and her clean, tidy life. And most of all it told me that I had probably come to realize this too late. She ran her fingers through Sailor A's curly hair then, clenched her fists, pulled him up to her by two handfuls of his thick, wavy locks and kissed him full on a mouth all shiny with her juices. There was a moment when she broke her gaze towards me to reach down and grab Sailor A's cock and place the head at the opening to her dripping cunt, where the usually fair hair was now completely dark and sodden with the various liquids of sex. As he entered her with a hard thrust, she gave a cry that I had never heard her utter before. It was more like an animal grunt or groan, not loud, but still I found it utterly compelling, and I was gripped by an intense pang of irrational jealousy. Again, her eyes lost mine and this time she broke our gaze entirely and I could see that she was entirely preoccupied by the activity that was taking place between her thighs. I watched as the twin pistons drove into her soft flesh, and then pulled out; the sailors had created a sort of rhythm to their thrusts and I wondered if they had done this double act before.

I moved over to where Birgit's head lolled on the shoulder of Sailor B. I stroked her cheek and she became aware of my presence. She reached for my cock and pulled me towards her mouth. She sucked me until I was hard again. Then she pushed off Sailor A and said, "It's your turn, Claude. Fuck me – fuck me like you've never fucked me before." I had never even heard her say the word "fuck" before and it had a galvanic effect.

The sensation was strange: I could smell the other man's sweat, the outside of my knees brushed his hairy thighs and I wondered if I was going to be able to go through with it. Then I was in and suddenly my cock was plunged deep into a fleshy turmoil, as if it were thrusting inside the guts of a squirming octopus, a strange convulsion of moving, rippling flesh. Only minutes later Sailor B groaned and yelled, "I'm there! I'm coming up her arse!" Birgit shuddered with pleasure.

"H", with its singular hump in one form, immediately gets us into hail and Horny mood. In capital mode, it stands domineeringly astride on its two stilts, which leads us rather appropriately (by the throat) on to High heels and Humiliation.

Heels Over Head

Well why not, if you're feeling energetic and agile. For her, it's not as tricky or uncomfortable as it looks; for him, the weight of her legs might hang heavy on his shoulders, but that deepness and power of penetration will take his mind off it. Psychologically, we are talking exposure, surrender, and powerlessness on her part, while he is at liberty to "take" her with full force. This is not a coupling for lingering over and offers only vaginal stimulation for her, so it's a good choice for a concluding coitus after a period of extended foreplay. However, it is a handy manoeuvre for making it in a car.

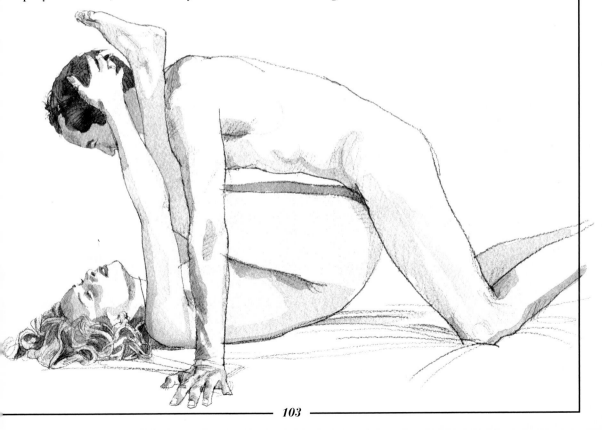

Handballing

Also known as fisting, fist-fucking (or FF for short), and puppeteering. This practice is strictly for the sexual gourmet with a taste for the exotic, and more than a few hours to spare; for those less-adventurous diners, it might put you off your bedtime cocoa. You can opt for vagina or anal, the former definitely being the softer, and safer, option, since it is demonstrably capable of expansion for childbirth. It is strongly advised to wear latex gloves to protect the vagina against any roughness of hand or fingernail, and plenty of water-based lubricant should be applied. Entry must be made extremely carefully and gradually, first opening up the vagina with two or three fingers before inserting the whole hand. Withdrawing the hand must also be done with care. The anus is an altogether different prospect, since it is not designed to expand in the same way. It is therefore necessary to work slowly and carefully at building up the expansion capacity of your partner's anus, which can be done with the use of thicker and thicker well-lubricated dildos. Removal again has to be undertaken with extreme caution because of the risk of a vacuum effect. I will leave you to ponder the names of some extreme fisting techniques: "to the elbow", "twisting", and "cleaning the bird".

Hetaerae

Life for women in Ancient Greece was a tough call, no matter at which particular lowly level of society they happened to find themselves. Athenian orator and statesman Demosthenes (4th century BC) neatly summed up the picture: "We keep hetaerae for the sake of pleasure, concubines for the daily requirements of the body, and wives to bear us legitimate children and to be the faithful guardians of our households." Well, we all know which we would have plumped for. Hetaerae were the high-class call-girls of the day, providing entertainment for the rich and famous – music, dance, a little poetry reading, and a stimulating line in rhetorical conversation – besides the usual sexual services. The fact that they had the means and opportunity to pursue an education is testament to their relatively privileged status, although they were still confined to their apartments.

High Heels

Some women like to wear high heels simply because it improves the proportions of their legs and generally makes them feel more feminine, and many men enjoy the resultant effect. Other women are obsessed with funky footwear, Imelda Marcos-style, and some men are equally fixated by same in mildly fetish vein. Then there is the SM scenario in which a woman brandishes a spiked heel in a threat of violence for the benefit of the submissive male, or the classic porn video-queen scene with the heroine using the heel of her shoe for lurid sexual gratification. In juxtaposition, we have the fully-fledged fetishist using the inside of a shoe as a substitute vagina. So, all in all, the humble shoe is one hell of a sex object, although I guess it doesn't work the same with trainers. There is also more than a whiff of bondage about footwear. One obvious example is the ancient Chinese cult of the bound foot, which had various erotic connotations, not least the restriction of movement. And this same dimension manifests in the hobbling or "crippling" effect of the high-heeled shoe.

Humiliation

This is the stuff of submission and domination sex games, for those who get their kicks out of delivering it and the others who do likewise in receipt. But it can often be an aspect of more conventional sexual practices in its mildest form. For instance, there are those who get an extra buzz in the heat of lovemaking when their partner lashes them with a few well-chosen words of abuse. Obviously, the key word here is consensual – it's no good to anyone if the insults prove to be a turn-off instead of a turn-on, or if your verbal lashing bites too deeply. It's probably fair to say that those who are genuinely confident in themselves with a relatively high self-esteem are more likely to be sexually aroused by being debased. In heavy-duty humiliation sex play, to add insult to insult, the submissive may be forced to do something degrading, such as performing a really menial task, or embarrassing, like wearing baby clothes. It may also involve bondage and the dominant partner urinating over the submissive other, or slapping a pie in their face.

The DuPret Collection

Summer's *Heat...*

In summer's **heat** and mid-time of the day
To rest my limbs upon a bed I lay,
One window shut, the other open stood,
Which gave such light, as twinkles in a wood,
Like twilight glimpse at setting of the sun,
Or night being past, and yet not day begun.
Such light to shamefast maidens must be shown,
Where they must sport, and seem to be unknown.
Then came Corinna in a long loose gown,
Her white neck hid with tresses hanging down:
Resembling fair Semiramis going to bed
Or Layis of a thousand wooers sped.
I snatched her gown, being thin, the harm was small,
Yet strived she to be covered there withal.
And striving thus as one that would be cast,
Betrayed herself, and yielded at the last.
Stark naked as she stood before mine eye,
Not one wen in her body could I spy.
What arms and shoulders did I touch and see,
How apt her breasts were to be pressed by me?
How smooth a belly under her waist saw I?
How large a leg, and what a lusty thigh?
To leave the rest, all liked me passing well,
I clinged her naked body, down she fell,
Judge you the rest, being tired she bade me kiss.
Jove send me more such afternoons as this.

"Elegy 5", Ovid (43 BC–AD c.17), translated by Christopher Marlowe

Peter Fendi (1796–1842)

H is for Harem

The Moorish Lady's Story

Anon

From a *Night in a Moorish Harem*. The Scarlet Library

"Ladies," she said, "you all know I am three months gone with child; you have now to learn what is equally true; I am still a virgin."

"A virgin and with child!" they all echoed, several of them crossing themselves as they exclaimed.

"Listen and you shall hear," proceeded Zuleika.

"I was purchased from my parents in Fez, where we lived, by a young Moorish merchant. They, as well as myself, were delighted at the prospects which he promised, to transfer me to the harem of some great Moorish Pasha. The price paid was very high as I was warranted a virgin. The next morning we joined the caravan for Morocco. Mounted on my camel, I enjoyed the trip in the highest spirits. Ali, my master, rode beside me on a fine horse which he managed with grace and vigour. His person was slender, and his features, which were at the same time bold and amiable, captured my fancy. His attentions to me were unremitting; his tent every night was pitched near my own to guard me from intrusion. The last night on the road I had retired early and was just sinking to sleep as the darkness fell, when Ali appeared in my tent.

"'What is your will, my lord?' I asked. He knelt down and kissed me; it was the first time he had done so.

"'My wish is to make you my wife,' he replied. 'And why should you not, my lord?' I asked again. Then he told me all his fortune was invested in my purchase, and that it would only bring poverty and misery on us both. We mingled our regrets and caresses, which now grew more and more ardent, until I found myself lying beneath him with my bosoms bared to his kisses and my naked thighs parted. Beneath them I felt a gentle pressure which penetrated the hair and touched the sensitive lips again.

"I lay passive with my eyes shut. A soft desire ran through my frame, and centring at the lips where Ali was pressing, and making the pressure delightful.

"The longer he continued in this position the more I wished for a deeper and more gratifying thrust.

"But the gentle pushes he gave barely parted the outside lips. I could feel that they were stopped by the virgin membrane that barred all further entrance. I grew with desire; I strained him to my bosom, and pressing my mouth to his, I was relieved of a melting thrill. At the same moment I felt Ali's answering throb and a gush of sperm penetrated to the depths of my loins, far within the still unbroken curtain of my virginity. For a long time we lay in a voluptuous but motionless repose. Then Ali tore himself away from my arms. 'I must go,' he said; 'I could not resist another such temptation.' It is three months since that sweet but imperfect connection, which is now certain will result in my being a mother."

"And has no man touched you since?" I asked, with the deeper interest, as I took the splendid Moorish girl in my arms.

"I can tell you," said Inez, "why the Pasha, who never before suffered a woman to remain a virgin a single night in his harem, has spared her. He purchased her from Ali on the day she arrived from Morocco. After having her examined by the old woman in his employ, she was brought here, and the same evening, as soon as he had finished his supper, he threw his handkerchief to her. She retired to receive him in her room alone, as only a virgin in this harem has the privilege of doing.

"For, as you already know, it is customary for us to receive the Pasha's embraces when we are all present. I noticed Zuleika looked very reluctant; she was no doubt thinking of Ali, from whom she had so recently parted. I overtook her at the door of the bridal chamber. 'Let me take your place for tonight,' said I; 'we are of the same size, and complexions will not show in the dark; the Pasha shall never know.'

"'Can you indeed manage it?' she asked; 'if so you are welcome.' Then she hurried away, and I entered the bridal chamber in her place, undressed, extinguished the light, and got into bed. Before a great while the Pasha came. He kissed me on the back of my neck, for I had buried my face in the pillow like a bashful girl. Then he hurriedly undressed, and stretching himself beside me, took me in his arms. My heart was beating violently for the success of my bold scheme. But this agitation he took for virgin fright. I answered in monosyllables to his questions, and shrank from every caress he bestowed on my bosom and thighs.

"He became, as I intended he should, only more eager. When at last he mounted me I covered my face with my hands as if in a paroxysm of shame, and wrapping one of my legs over the other I held them tightly together. He had to lie with his thighs parted over mine. In this position he guided his crest between them, worked its way among the hair, and began to enter the tightly squeezed lips beneath.

"My passion had become so thoroughly aroused by this time that I could scarcely help opening my thighs and letting him have free entrance. My monthly period was just passing off, in the latter part of which a woman is peculiarly susceptible to desire. But I made him gain his way by the hardest pushing. Not only were my thighs locked but I concentrated the muscles of my sheath at the lips. He would give a fierce but ineffective thrust; then he would squeeze and suck my bosom; until at last my wantonness became uncontrollable and I gave way with a rapture that unnerved me as I let his shaft plunge in to the hilt. He spent profusely with a long sigh of triumphant satisfaction. I gave a sigh equally profound; I could not help it. But it only completed his delusion, for he thought it was caused by the pain I suffered at the loss of my maiden-head.

He petted and consoled me with kisses and caresses until we were both ready for another embrace. This time he did not expect to encounter any resistance. He met with none, though I took care to be sufficiently coy at his embrace. Then he fell asleep. I know he would wake in the morning with a stiff shaft, so just before dawn, I went and took a bath, put on my most seductive apparel, and adorned myself with musk. Soon I heard him call: 'Zuleika! Zuleika!' I hastened to his bedside.

"'Zuleika begs that you will excuse her, my lord,' said I; 'pray have some mercy on the poor girl.' Then I turned down the sheet and exposed the blood stains occasioned by my monthly period. 'See,' said I, 'you have butchered her.' 'Then you must come to bed,' he replied.

"This was just what I sought, and I lost no time in doing so. For the third time I got all I wanted."

The sedate and upright form of the capital "I" belies the sexual turmoil that lurks within, perhaps a little betrayed by its quirky lower case form — an unwanted ill (Inhibition) and a carnal sin (Incest). This is where Innocence is well and truly lost...

In The Air

We have lift off! This position is known as "flying angel" – a term that would seem to make light of the heroics involved. There is no getting away from the fact that both partners have to be strong and fit to try this coupling, but a lot of women as well as men work out and this is a great opportunity to put those muscles to creative erotic use. She can help to secure her hold by hooking one foot around the other in order to lock her ankles together behind his back. In any case, she needs to be a comparative featherweight. There are times when we just have to do something extravagant sexually – not when we're desperate to come but when we have the latitude to go wild, experiment and grab some passionate fun. The opportunity for serious thrusting is limited here and it's got to be a quickie, however strong you are, but you could always move on to a nearby chair or table for the final consummation. A cheat's version is straight off to head for a piece of furniture on which she can perch, like the back of a heavy armchair, with one leg on terra firma and the other clasped around his upper thigh.

Inhibition Most of us are likely to have been hampered sexually by some form of inhibition or another. A common stumbling block is being embarrassed about one or other aspects of our bodies. Women can be plagued by all kinds of hang-ups in this respect – unevenly sized breasts, moles in strange places, large, protruding labia minora, to pluck just a few from the air. Men, on the other hand, inevitably worry about not only the size but appearance of their penises – over-bent, unevenly pigmented – and scrotums. The reason for all this anxiety may well stem from the fact that we are on the whole deprived of images of uncloaked ordinary folk in their myriad shapes and sizes with which we could comfortable compare and reassure ourselves. But over and above this is the problem of not being able to let go or fulfil our sexual desires, which could be related to the aforementioned, or the result of shyness, timidity, or feelings of guilt, stress, and the pressure of everyday concerns, or because of negative experiences in the past. This is where developing mind fantasies can help to provide a trigger to release us into our own erotic pleasure domes.

Ithyphallic This term is generally used to denote depictions of the erect penis in sculpture or graphic art. While they may not abound in contemporary or modern art, there was an awful lot of it about in prehistoric and classical times. Great Britain was fair bristling with phallic standing stones in the days of yore, with Celtic culture championing the power of the penis. The cult of the erect member was a prominent feature of Egyptian mythology, with the gods Osiris, Amen-Ra, and Min regularly sporting stiffies. But the phallus truly came into its own in Ancient Greece. Huge sculptured or carved phalluses were paraded as part of the festivals held in honour of Dionysus. However, it was the divinity Priapus that put the other gods in the shade with his giant erection which exceeded his own height.

Jean-Baptiste Regnault (1754-1829)

Innocence Lost...

I gently touched her hand: she gave
A look that did my soul ensalve;
I pressed her rebel lips in vain;
They rose up to be pressed again.
Thus happy, I no farther meant,
Than to be pleased and innocent.

On her soft breasts my hand I laid,
And a quick, light impression made;
They with a kindly warmth did glow,
And swelled, and seemed to overflow.
Yet, trust me, I no farther meant,
Than to be pleased and innocent.

On her eyes my eyes did stay:
O'er her smooth limbs my hands did stray;
Each sense was ravished with delight,
And my soul stood prepared for flight.
Blame me not if at last I meant
More to be pleased than innocent.

Anon (17th Century)

Peter Fendi (1796–1842)

I is for Illicit Sex

Snow Bound

Elizabeth Coldwell

Forum magazine

The snow started coming down just outside Catterick. Just small, fluffy flakes at first, but soon they were falling with real intensity, the windscreen wipers struggling to push them away. As John concentrated on the little he could see of the road ahead, I turned the radio to a local station, hoping to hear a weather bulletin. It wasn't long in coming, and the forecast was not good: roads on higher ground were likely to become impassable and motorists were being urged not to travel unless their journey was strictly necessary.

I looked at John anxiously. This had not been in the plan. We had been travelling around the area all day, scouting locations for a psychological thriller that the production company for which we worked was making for the BBC, and, having found the perfect farmhouse on the outskirts of the village of Middleham, were hoping to be back in London some time before December 23 slipped over into Christmas Eve. This unexpected snowstorm meant that wasn't going to happen.

"What do you reckon?" I asked

John's face looked tired. "We're not going to make it to London, Lisa, that's for sure. We'll see if we can get as far as York, look for a hotel there. I know it's Christmas, but I'm sure someone will have a couple of rooms." His voice didn't sound hopeful.

He pulled the car over to the side of the road and reached for his mobile phone. "I'd better ring Amanda. Let her know my plans have changed."

I turned away, not wanting to eavesdrop on his conversation with his wife. It was common knowledge around the office that their marriage ran far from smoothly.

Trying to ignore John's increasingly desperate explanations of the situation, I stared out of the car window. The snow seemed to be easing slightly, and I realized we had pulled up in front of a house that had a sign at the bottom of the garden which read "Honeysuckle Cottage Bed and Breakfast".

John slammed his phone shut, his expression grim.

"What happened?" I asked.

"She went ballistic. She accused me of making up a story so I can stay away overnight, and told me she knows all about my 'sordid affair'. I wouldn't be surprised if I got home tomorrow and found she's changed the locks and filed for divorce."

I decided not to try to work out whether he was joking. Instread, I said, "Well, we've had a stroke of luck. We're parked right outside a B&B."

"Funny place to have one," John replied, "out here in the back end of nowhere."

"You'd be surprised," I said. "Lots of people come out walking in the Dales in the summer, or they come for the races. I bet a place like this must do a roaring trade."

Despite my confidence, it didn't seem that way as we stood on the doorstep. There didn't appear to be a light on in the house, and John banged on the door repeatedly, hoping to raise a response. Just as we were about to give up and leave, the door creaked open a fraction and a woman's face appeared.

"You don't have a couple of rooms available, by any chance?" John asked, smiling at her.

"I'm sorry, I'm not taking guests,"she replied. "We always shut over Christmas."

"That's okay…," John began, turning away,

but her expression seemed to change, as though she had seen the filthy weather outside her front door for the first time.

"No, no," she said, opening the door wider. "Come in. I hadn't realized it was snowing. You'll have to take the place as you find it, and I only have the one room, but…"

I glanced at John. Sharing a room hadn't been part of the equation. "That's not a problem, is it, Lisa?" he said. I shook my head.

As the landlady led us down the hall, I got a good look at her for the first time. She was wearing a paisley-patterned minidress and pale blue tights, and with her bobbed blonde hair and pale lipstick, she looked like a Sixties dolly bird. Given the décor of the house, she didn't appear remotely out of place.

She led us up the stairs, turned right along the landing, and unlocked a door. "Here you go," she said. "The bathroom is next door. I'll have to turn the immersion heater on, so don't expect any hot water for an hour or so."

The room smelt musty, as though it had been closed up for some time, and the bed, when I sat on it, was soft. I couldn't imagine getting a good night's sleep here.

"I know what's really worrying you," John said, coming to sit beside me. "It's what Amanda would think if she knew we were sharing a bed. Well, she's not going to know about it."

He put his arm around me, and gave me a friendly squeeze. Despite myself, I began to relax into his embrace. For a moment, I almost forgot he was my married boss, and strictly off-limits. Then there was a knock at the door, and I sprang away from him guiltily.

"Come in," he called, and the landlady entered, carrying a tray which bore two plates, two glasses, and a bottle of wine.

"There you go," she said, setting it down.

"What do we owe you?" John asked, reaching in his back pocket for his wallet.

"Oh, we'll settle up in the morning," she replied cheerfully. "Just leave the tray outside the door when you've finished."

With that, she was gone. We fell on the contents of the tray ravenously. It was nothing elaborate, just a simple chicken salad and some bread, but lunch had been a sandwich eaten in the car somewhere outside Ripon, and we were both starving. Given the general ambience of Honeysuckle Cottage, it didn't surprise me in the least that the wine was Liebfraumilch. Sweet and slightly warm as it was, it still hit the spot.

"I think I'll go and see if there's any hot water," I said. "I could do with a soak in the tub; my shoulders are stiff from sitting in the car for so long."

"It's not a bath you need, it's a massage," John replied. "Come here."

There's nothing worse than having someone who doesn't know what they're doing prodding t your flesh. but John was good, his fingers skilfully teasing out the knots in my muscles.

"This is nice," I said, "but I'm sure it would be doing me more good if your fingers were touching my skin. I feel like my T-shirt's getting in the way."

John could not have failed to work out that when his fingers traced over my back there was no outline of a bra. The implication of what I'd said was obvious. For a long moment I thought I'd misjudged the situation and made a terrible fool of myself. Then, his voice thick with unmistakable desire, he murmured, "Take it off, then."

My back still to him, I pulled the hem of my long-sleeved T-shirt out of my jeans. Before I could turn and show him just how excited I already was, his hands were on my skin again, but this time moving down my back and round to cup my breasts. His fingers rolled and pinched my nipples.

I shouldn't be doing this, I knew that, and yet I couldn't stop myself. It was longer than I cared to think since I'd last been with a man, and certainly since I'd been with anyone who knew how to push my buttons the way John did. His hands were on the waistband of my jeans, unfastening the button, sliding down the zip, and working their way into my lacy underwear.

Without warning, he flipped me face down on the bed, pulling down my jeans and panties in one movement until they were down round my knees and my bottom was bared to him. I tried to struggle to a kneeling position, but he ordered me to stay where I was. The next thing I felt was his hand landing squarely on my backside. I yelped, and prayed the landlady couldn't hear me.

I'd never had John marked down as being into spanking, but then sex as a topic had never been discussed between us.

His hand slammed down again and again, stinging my cheeks. It hurt, more than I could have imagined, and I found myself begging him to stop. But then his fingers sneaked down to lightly touch my clitoris, and I almost screamed. What he was doing to me seemed to have muddled all my nerve-endings up, so that the dull, throbbing pain in my blotchy backside was somehow fuelling the sweet pleasure of having my clit played with. I wriggled, trying to spread my legs wider and get a better contact between his fingers and my hard little nub, but he had other ideas and pulled his hand away.

"Please, I want to come." I was aware of a whining tone in my voice.

"Not till I say so," he replied. "If I say so."

I was already strung out, on the brink of climax, and needing only the merest of touches to take me over the edge. The thought that John might choose to leave me there, unsatisfied, was too horrible to contemplate…

"J" is a generous character, offering something for him (Jerking off) and something for her (Jade Stalk, and I think you can guess what that is). But i also adds a twist in the tale for us all — that sexual demon, Jealousy.

Jerking Off

Most of us have to rely on a quick solo hand job to keep ourselves from going mad with frustration or boredom, or both, locked as we invariably are into one or other of the sex-free zones of work and domestic duty. But what joy to treat yourself to a full-scale, luxurious wank, stripping off and setting up the mirror at the right level for the occasion. That never fails to heighten the excitement. Take your time to build up to orgasm, experimenting with different grips and varying the pace or employing a stop-go approach. Perhaps even deny yourself the ultimate ecstasy as a prelude to lovemaking. But can we watch?

Jealousy Why is it that we can happily toy with another, convincing ourselves that it doesn't "mean anything" in comparison to our central relationship, but that should we find our significant other engaging in extra-curricular activities on the same basis, we would be sick to the stomach with jealousy. Sometimes we need to experience that nasty stabbing pain to refocus our attention in the right direction. However, there are those that use jealousy specifically to trigger the adrenalin rush as a sexual stimulant – a nice trick if you can handle it. This is often a feature of group sex or swinging scenes. It is also quite common, in the case of male escorts or gigolos, for men to hire their services in order to witness them having sexual contact with their female partners.

Joy of Sex *Joy of Sex: A Gourmet Guide to Lovemaking*, to give it its full title, written by Dr Alex Comfort, was first published in 1972 and succeeded in making real sex for real people at long last respectable at the same time as enjoyable. It was a phenomenal success, with some eight million copies to its credit. Although updated many times, many of us still recall with fondness its hallmark original illustrations – the sepia-toned sketchy drawings of the nice, non-macho, post-hippy dude with the beard and dishevelled hair, his partner well-matched but sans beard; all very non-threatening. And then there was the playful extended metaphor on the gourmet theme of the subtitle, with chapters on "Ingredients" (body parts and other general issues); "Appetizers" or "Starters", depending on your side of the pond (foreplay); with "Main Courses" to follow, and "Sauces and Pickles" on the side. The 1991 update contained an additional chapter on AIDS, but otherwise much of its approach has stood the test of time remarkably well. Dr Comfort's son Nick has now picked up the baton with a complete makeover for the nearly-new millennium.

Since We Your Husband Daily See

Since we your husband daily see
So **jealous** out of season,
Phyllis, let you and I agree
To make him so with reason.

I'm vexed to think that every night
A sot within thy arms
Tasting the most divine delight
Should sully all your charms.

While fretting I must lie alone
Cursing the powers divine
That undeservedly have thrown
A pearl unto a swine.

Then, Phyllis, heal my wounded heart,
My burning passion cool;
Let me at least in thee have part
With thy insipid fool.

Let him by night his joys pursue
And blunder in the dark,
While I by day enjoying you
Can see to hit the mark.

Matthew Prior (1664–1721)

The Onlooker, Thomas Rowlandson (1756–1827)

J is for Juices

The Oyster

Anon

Molly was by now idly running her cool hands up and down my thighs, and we were both soon squirming around on the bed. Leaning over me, she kissed me fully on the lips before transferring her tongue to my ear which sent shivers all through my body, especially when she started to press my titties between her fingers which intensified the tingling sensation tremendously.

By now my whole body was shaking with lust and when Molly began stroking my pussy I grasped her hand and pushed it firmly between my legs, which I squeezed together, crushing her hand between them. She understood my urgent need for she let her head slide down from my ear to my tummy and into my black thatch of pussy hair. She parted my lips with her fingers and slipped her tongue into my wet cunny, licking all around the edge with the tip before thrusting it all the way in. She was teasing my pussy to unbelievable heights, using tongue and fingers to spread my wetness all round my cunt. I just closed my eyes and let myself dissolve into a glorious sea of lubricity as her teeth now nibbled along my cunny lips whilst her pink little tongue teased my clitty with long, rasping licks. Up and down. in and out her long tongue lapped up my slippery juices as, by now totally abandoned, I threw my legs high up upon her shoulders.

Now I could feel myself begin to experience the first sensations of a spend build up inside me. "Oh Anna, your juices taste so delicious. I love sucking your juicy cunny," gasped Molly, diving back again to give me the final *coup de grace*. She lashed her tongue against my clitty, rubbing it until it stuck out between my lips. Then she wrenched her mouth from my sopping muff and replaced it with her fingers, finding my swollen clitty, which she tugged only for a few seconds before I was away! My body thrashed wildly about in a frenzied ecstasy as her finger slid into my bum-hole. I exploded into an uncontrollable spasm of excitement and my juices flowed freely as I reached a gigantic peak of orgasmic lust.

Molly and I writhed about in each other's arms, our breasts crushed together, our tawny titties rubbing against each other as we kissed feverishly. Now it was my turn to make Molly spend and she laid back expectantly as I kissed her stalky red nipples with their saucer-like brown aureoles, drawing circles with my tongue. flicking the nipples up to a ripe hardness. Then I kissed her belly all the way down to that soft, golden nest…

Dipping my face close so that I could nuzzle into that silky blonde pussy, I licked my fingers and separated her folds, inhaling the tangy feminine odour of her dripping slit. Spreading her lips with my tongue, I explored her sopping pussy, gauging her responses, then sliding my arms around her thighs I adjusted my position and relaxed into flowing movements with my head, my tongue nudging her clitty, pushing against the hood. Her pelvis set the tempo, coming to meet me faster and faster as I increased the speed, pressing down with my teeth as she began to toss from side to side.

"Oh, Anna, that's marvellous. Oh yes, oh yes! Now darling, finger me," she panted. "Finish me off with your fingers." She put her hands on her inner thighs and pulled her legs apart, revealing her fleshy pink outer lips. She was so swollen and wet that she hardly noticed three of my fingers slide into her sopping cunny. But she certainly did when I started to work up a pacey rhythm, working my fingers in and out, slowly at first, then faster as she got wetter and wetter. She now frigged her clitty at the same time, working the little rosebud around with her thumb and forefinger. I straddled her and whilst I jerked one hand in and out of her pussy I roughly tweaked her titties with the other making her moan with pleasure and she spent profusely, shrieking so loudly with delight that I was afraid we might be disturbed.

Well, dear readers, we were indeed disturbed. What we had failed to hear in our haste was the sound of a ladder being placed against the window and the thwack of the window cleaner's shoes as he climbed up the rungs to undertake his duties. Molly suddenly shot out of bed and grabbed a towel to cover herself as she padded towards the window.

"Anna, look outside, we have an unannounced guest!" said Molly fiercely, opening the window to drag in a young man of about 23 who was still clutching his washleather.

"I have an excellent idea. You can make up for your intrusion by lending us your cock for the next 30 minutes. I have a great fancy for a fuck whilst I am sure that Anna would also be interested in seeing what you have to offer."

He blushed shyly and said: "Nothing would please me more, but I feel so nervous that I don't know whether I will be able to…"

"Oh don't worry about all that, we'll get you in the mood, have no fear. Now you go and undress and take a quick shower. When you come back we'll be ready for you," commanded Molly.

Richard, for that was his name, came back into the room. "Come and join us, there's no need to be shy," I said, as the young man still held back. He smiled and dropping the towel which was draped around his waist, he walked towards us. He certainly was blessed with a thick stalk between his legs, but though it was swinging heavily, it was far from being ready for business, but as I judged at the time, he only needed a little encouragement to light the fire.

For how quickly things changed when we got Richard on to the bed between us. We rolled him over on to his back and I sat across his knees while Molly sat perched on his chest. I took hold of his prick in my hand and it immediately swelled up under my soft touch. I knelt down and rubbed my breasts and nipples over this stiff shaft and then took the gleaming helmet into my mouth and began sucking noisily upon it as Molly moved up to place her pussy over his mouth so that he could tongue her cunny. Molly was making throaty noses as his tongue probed inside her cunny lips. His now huge prick was more than a mouthful for me as I sucked away on his knob, caressing his shaft until it was as stiff as iron. Then I shifted myself and lowered my wet cunt over his pulsating penis. I sank down gratefully, feeling the ivory column penetrate deeper and deeper inside me. Molly and I bounced up and down on poor Richard in unison and together we wriggled atop our young stud and I could feel waves of arousal taking me over.

After a minute of two of this treatment he removed his face from Molly's pussy and let out a growl. I felt his cock throb wildly and shoot out a rivulet of frothy white spunk as he spent copiously, the hot love juice filling my cunny and running down my thighs. A considerate and thoughtful man, Richard recovered himself enough to keep stimulating Molly's pussy with his tongue while his fingers now sought my clitty to finish me off. Molly came quite quickly and he lapped up her love juices as she spent copiously over his face.

"I can't get there without a cock in my cunt," I said regretfully as I did not believe that Richard was capable of raising any interest for a while. But happily he proved me wrong as the young sportsman simply gave his cock a swift shake and I was amazed to see it swell up to its former flagpole-like state. I took hold of it in my hand and found that such was the girth that I needed two hands to grasp the thick pole. Molly made way for me to lie on my back and Richard threw himself across me. He took his monster cock in one hand and drove home. I could feel it stretching my muscles beyond any previous capacity and I experienced a fulfilment that was simply divine and the thought flashed through my mind that as nice as the little tribadistic episode had been with Molly, nothing could beat the sensation of a big fat prick up one's cunny. Ah, what bliss! Every millimetre of my nook tingled to the pumping of his surging shaft as his wrinkled hairy ballsack bounced against my bum.

"Oh you big-cocked boy! Fuck my juicy cunt with your thick prick!" I panted as he thrust home, sliding his shaft in and out of my squelchy wetness. Several times I thought he was on the point of spunking yet somehow he held back until I was ready for him. Again and again, faster and faster he pounded in and out of my crack until my lips emitted one long, hoarse wail as I climaxed again and again in a seemingly multiple orgasm.

Then, suddenly, he pulled out and reared over me. He grabbed his prick hard, giving it two or three convulsive jerks until a huge squirt of salty sperm spouted out, arcing towards my breasts, splashing my nipples, streaming down my belly, and into my curly bush.

"*K*" *is a highly physical letter, so be prepared for a punishing workout. The Knee-trembler is just a warm-up for the acrobatic antics of the Kama Sutra, finishing with a few Kegel exercises. After all that, you'll settle for a few gentle Kisses.*

Knee-trembler

This manoeuvre is an absolute necessity for those emergency situations when you simply have to fuck but space, time and opportunity are in limited supply. Alternatively, the spontaneous, urgent character of this form of coupling may have its appeal in a conventional context, as a contrast to more routine, fully naked approaches. The degree of knee-tremble to be endured (not that you'll notice much in the heat of your passion) will depend on your comparative heights. If she is tall, so much the better, otherwise she will be at full stretch on tiptoes and he will be crouching. Whatever the case and for either party, those leg muscles are going to be in for a hammering in order to effect sufficient thrust. But the resulting gratification will be well worth a little post-coital cramp. However, if you have the opportunity, why not lessen the agony by using a nearby wall or pillar as a support, so that he can actually hoist her off the ground. A tree might be a more opportunistic prop, since this is an ideal deployment for alfresco sex. In addition to the usual precautions in the interests of discretion and privacy, keep well away from people walking their dogs since the attendant heady scents might prove too much of a draw if you happen to be downwind of a passing pooch.

Kabazzah This ancient Eastern technique, which features in Tantric sex, is one that can only be perfected (and then after much dedicated practice) once a woman has toned up her PC muscle (see "Kegel Exercises" opposite). In this instance, all the hard work is done by her, while he remains passive. The idea is to tense and release the PC muscle in a rhythmic sequence, in the action of "milking" the penis. The trusty *Kama Sutra* (see below) offers a suitable sexual position, called "The Pair of Tongs". Here, the woman sits astride the lying man, with her knees bent back, and squeezes away. This form of coupling has the added advantage of facilitating fondling of the clitoris either by him (to keep awake) or her.

Kama Sutra This amazing book remains, despite the passage of a very long time since its creation somewhere around the 1–5th century AD, the seminal sex manual. Sanskrit for "Aphorisms of Love", the Kama Sutra was written by one Vatsyayana in ancient India, about whom we apparently know precious little. Brit explorer Sir Richard Burton happily picked it up on his travels, and translated and privately published it back in England in 1883. We tend to think of it just in terms of all those impossibly acrobatic sex positions with exotic titles (I don't somehow think that "The Highest-Yawning Congress" implies boredom), but there's an awful lot to do before you can get on to the main business. We start, just for a warm-up, with five types of kissing – straight, bent, turned, pressed, and gently pressed. Then we move on to the eight types of biting, which include the eye-watering "biting of the boar". Alternatively, or as well as, you could choose from the eight kinds of pressing, marking, or scratching with the nails – the "peacock's foot" sounds worth a try. Along with chapters on "Acquiring a Wife", "Relations with Other Men's Wives", and "Courtesans", there's a section entitled "On the Means of Attracting Others to One's Self", which features a handy guide to increasing the size of the penis or contracting the vagina.

Kegel Exercises

These don't require a trip to the gym or any expensive workout kit and yet the benefits are there for all to grab. We have Dr Arnold Kegel to thank for them, although he didn't necessarily have the sex angle in his sights. He discovered that by exercising the pubococcygeus, or PC, muscle, women could improve their bladder control and strengthen their pelvic floor, particularly after childbirth when this is weakened. Pelvic floor exercises are now standard for post-pregnant women but it's taken some time for the advantages of these for everyone, men and women, to be broadcast – namely, increased strength and control of the vagina and penis. The PC is easy to get acquainted with – just stop peeing in mid flow and you'll have made your first introductions. But this is for recognition purposes only; repeatedly interrupting urination could cause problems. So, once you're on nodding terms with your PC, it's basically a case of tense, hold for 3–5 seconds, then release. Try out your new-found penile strength by seeing if you can hang a hand towel or tea towel from your member and give a little wave, or women can test their vaginal grip on a pencil (the floor-show stunt is to "smoke" a cigarette, but this is not to be recommended).

Kokigami

I have always felt that a "how-to" book on cock crafts would go down a storm. And now it's happened, with the advent of Kokigami – the art of penis adornment by way of paper sculpture (see page 319). If the term sounds familiar, that's because it's closely related to the beloved pastime of Christmas Day afternoons and sometime cure for insomniacs, Origami – the art of paper folding. However, it appears that Kokigami actually originates from the ancient Japanese art of Tsutsumi, in which men would decoratively wrap their members in ribbons and silks before retiring to their bedchambers, where their womenfolk would have great fun opening up their "presents". The idea was to play out the proceedings, and the pleasure, in making the wrapping as intricate as possible. And we end up with Origami for kicks!

Kama Sutra

Kisses Loathsome

I abhor the slimie kisse,
(Which to me most loathsome is.)
Those lips please me which are plac't
Close, but not too strictly lac't:
Yeilding I wo'd have them; yet
Not a wimbling Tongue admit:
What sho'd poking-sticks make there,
When the ruffe is set elsewhere?

Robert Herrick (1591–1674)

Stolen Kisses, Thomas Rowlandson (1756–1827)

K is for Kiss Sex

No Tongues

Stephen Bayley

Many husbands are familiar with that grudging but nonetheless welcome acceptance of a badly timed amorous advance, "OK, but be quick, don't sweat, and no kissing."

It is not the speed, nor the sweat, but the kissing that is interesting here. Whereas penetrative sex may be what men are said to think about 26 times a minute, sometimes more, it is significant that their partners tend (eventually) to attribute less significance to the predictable motions of the pistons and cylinders in sexual mechanics than to the more subtle and delicate operations of the lips and the mouth. One gathers that prostitutes charge more for kissing than for how's-your-father because they believe it is more intimate. A peck on the lips, then, isn't business, it's *personal*.

The kiss is unique, or at least unusual, in the repertoire of Eros, because it is both affectionate and sexual. There is no ambiguity about copulation. It is a blatant expression: lust made slippery and tangible and convulsive. Sex of the sort that operates between the hips and the knees is in and out, up and down. Sex is black or white. Kissing, however, is on a grey scale of infinite variety. We kiss children and grannies one way, friends another, and lovers in a different style altogether.

Oral intercourse is common to most birds and quadrupeds, evidence of the significance of the mouth in non-verbal communication. Deep in the thick soup of DNA, kissing may share an original significance with biting; some male animals use their teeth the more firmly to grasp their partners while mating. I haven't tried this myself, although this prehistoric notion may contribute some of its primal force to that suspicion, hardening occasionally into a conviction, amongst many men that women to whom they are not married are inclined to bite and scream. Whereas women to whom they are married are more inclined, while on the job, to sigh and look longingly at their watches.

Despite the near-universal nature of kissing in animal behaviour, its significance in civilization seems to be more culturally specific. The Ancient Greek poets scarcely mention it, and whereas Attic vases show every variation of genital use you can imagine and some perhaps you cannot, I have never seen one showing a couple kissing.

Equally, the Celtic languages have no word for the kiss, although they may well have had many different words for bardic versions of the foregoing. But it is the far Orientals who are most ill-disposed to tongue-wrestling. Reporting from *fin-de-siècle* Japan, the traveling exotic, Lafcadio Hearn, said, "Kisses and embraces are simply unknown…as tokens of affection." In fact, mothers threatened their misbehaving children with a consuming and sloppy white man's kiss.

But in the nearer East, the *Kama Sutra* and *The Perfumed Garden* accept kissing as one of erotic love's more sophisticated expressive forms. The European Middle Ages saw the development of what we might call the modern kiss, although significantly it is considered a lofty refinement in the act of love, more likely practised by aristocrats than peasants. A medieval ballad called the *Glasgerion* tells the minatory story of a high-born woman who eventually realizes that she was bedded by a churl rather than a nobleman because while he efficiently "got her with child" (as churls do), he never bothered to kiss her.

In contemporary Europe, the kiss has become a universal norm, except in Lapland where they seem to prefer noses. (This may be something to do with ambient temperatures around the Arctic Circle, which tend to discourage the frivolous exposure of mucus membrane.)

Cesare Lombroso states that the exhilaration of the erotic kiss derives from the oral associations of nipples and motherhood, thus transcending in its meaningful complexity even the rich, dark puzzle of sex itself. Our own slight reluctance to discuss kissing suggests a reticence that is based on something very primitive indeed. Syncopated, mutually penetrative oral sex may not replace the more fundamental sort, but it can be a powerfully stimulating prelude to the most effective forms of lubricious exchange whose rhythms, encounters, and intimacies it so accurately apes.

Space does not allow even a brief catalogue of the possible variations, although the powerful, flexible, and articulate tongue, with its roll, pitch, and yaw facilities, is better equipped to explore than the brute penis. Quite literally, a deep, committed kiss (the French call what we call a French kiss, "*Un baiser très appuyé*", or well-applied) short-circuits those carefully mapped neural pathways which link the contours of sex to the heights of taste and, by association, to smell.

The social phenomenon of air kissing – the mwah-mwah rituals of restaurant and party encounters – may be derived from ancient olfactory sniffing, the sort dogs do around bitches' bottoms. Swahili folk have an amusing variation on this. It is, one gathers, customary for pubescent boys to raise their garments and expose themselves to society ladies who will then smell the offered member in a charming ritual called "giving tobacco".

Smoking is, of course, the one thing that corrupts the pleasure of kissing; Swahili or no, few enjoy the sensation of deep-throating an ashtray. If you really want to pass biological matter from mouth to mouth, I'd recommend a nice old-fashioned burgundy. Meanwhile, be aware next time you visit a Japanese restaurant that you won't find tongue sushi on the menu.

This article first appeared in The Erotic Review *(see page 319).*

"*L*" is the key letter of our alphabet, since "*L*" is for *Love*, but it's also for its racier cousin, *Lust*. Sitting comfortably on the baseline as a capital, "*L*" appropriately brings us *Lap* sex (and why not *Lap* dancing while we're at it), while in its wonderfully fluid lower case form, it offers not only *Love* potions but *Lubricants*.

Lap Sex The only problem with this approach is finding the right chair. Priority number one: make sure it's sturdy enough and stable! And you don't want anything with arms, which will get in the way of her knees, plus it needs to be at the right height because she has to use her toes and legs for leverage, to bounce up and down. In fact, this position demands some decent leg muscles to get the best out of it. However, it also provides an ideal opportunity for some hypnotic, rhythmic grinding, which makes a nice change. Either way, psychologically for her it's great to have a good ride and the whip hand, and it's exciting for him to be so cruelly "used".

Libido Ah, the well-known lament of the lost libido. None of us, alas, are immune from this infliction, given that sexual desire can be influenced by a whole range of factors, both physical and psychological, which are the normal hazards of everyday life (whatever that is). In any case, individuals naturally have different levels of sex drive, and often the difficulties set in when we feel concerned – bombarded as we often are by idealized sexual scenarios – that we are in some way "abnormal". It is all too easy to feel inadequate and outfaced when confronted by examples of effortless supersex. There are of course specific medical conditions and medications that can affect libido, but we must be careful not to confuse impotence in men (inability to achieve/maintain an erection) with low lobido (sexual appetite), which is guaranteed to make things worse. Then there are the well-documented effects of the female menopause – but some men, too, can suffer in similar ways. And that brings us to the whole vexed area of hormonal treatment, which appears to raise as many questions as it provides answers. But for many of us, it is often outside pressures – money, work, family – which impact first and foremost on our emotional relationships, which in turn create emotional difficulties, and sex bows out from the bedroom.

Lolita Vladimir Nabokov's novel, first published in France in 1955 by the Olympia Press and subsequently banned by the French government of the day, rocked the Western world with its explosive, taboo subject matter – that of the sexual liaison between a 40-something man with a penchant for "nymphets" and the 12-year-old Dolores ("Lolita") Haze. Perverse, tragic, and comic it may have been, but the book was far from salacious and received the critical claim it deserved from the discerning of its readership on both sides of the pond. Later, in 1962, Stanley Kubrick was inspired to bring the concept to the big screen, with James Mason in the role of the doomed Humbert Humbert. In the interests of public sensibilities, Lolita (Sue Lyon) was raised to high-school age.

Love Potions

All manner of weird concoctions have been created down the centuries in the pursuit of sexual stimulation or the securing of undying love. Most have largely been discredited, deemed at best harmless and at worst downright poisonous if taken in any significant quantity. It all smacks of quackery and corruption. How else did they get people to believe in the efficacy of such wretched substances as rhinoceros horn? By choosing something so vile and so difficult (expensive) to obtain that it just had to work! A considerably cheaper option was a bodily fluid – semen or urine (what else) – judiciously employed to secure the affections of a favoured one. At least alcohol, in its conventional forms, is agreeable, although it is no guarantor of performance. As Shakespeare wisely noted, "It provokes the desire, but it takes away the performance". The monks of Continental Europe spent many a contented century cooking up some charming alcoholic beverages – Chartreus and Benedictine to name a couple – and had the decency to bequeath us the recipes. Among the more lethal stuff is Spanish Fly, a drug made from a beetle that produces major itching and only possibly an erection, and Mandrake (beloved of the 17th century metaphysical poets), a root used to make potent, narcotic potions.

Lubricants

"Lubes", as they are affectionately known, are big business these days. We are encouraged to slap them on at every opportunity for enhanced comfort and pleasure. However, it isn't that straightforward and one has to mind what one uses where. Oil-based lubricants are a no-no with condoms, since they can damage them; water-based varieties are therefore the appropriate lubes for the vagina. Oil- and petroleum-based products are the lubes of choice for anal play and masturbation but cannot be used with condoms. However, there are also water-based anal options, and some come with a handy applicator for in-depth delivery. Various novelty lubes are now available, to add to the fun. Edible fruit- and mint-flavoured lubes are specially designed for oral sex.

Eric Wilkins (Contemporary)

Lolitas? *Eric Wilkins (Contemporary)*

Love...

*Make love now, by night and by day, in winter
and in summer... You are in the world for that
and the rest of life is nothing but vanity,
illusion, waste. There is only one science, love,
only one riches, love, only one policy, love.
To make love is all the law, and the prophets.*

Anatole France

Mihaly von Zichy (1827-1906)

L is for Lysistrata

Lysistrata

From *Aristophanes* (410 BC)

Cleonice: *And why do you summon us, dear Lysistrata? What is it all about?*

Lysistrata: *About a big thing.*

Cleonice: *(taking this in a different sense; with great interest) And is it thick too?*

Lysistrata: *Yes, very thick.*

Cleonice: *And we are not all on the spot! Imagine!*

Lysistrata: (wearily) Oh! if it were what you suppose, there would be never an absentee. No, no, it concerns a thing I have turned about and about this way and that so many sleepless nights.

Cleonice: (still unable to be serious) It must be something mighty fine and subtle for you to have turned it about so!

Lysistrata: So fine, it means just this, Greece saved by the women!

Cleonice: By the women! Why, its salvation hangs on a poor thread then!

Lysistrata: Our country's fortunes depend on us – it is with us to undo utterly the Peloponnesians.

Cleonice: That would be a noble deed truly!

Lysistrata: To exterminate the Boeotians to a man!

Cleonice: But surely you would spare the eels.

Lysistrata: For Athens' sake I will never threaten so fell a doom; trust me for that. However, if the Boeotian and Peloponnesian women join us, Greece is saved.

Cleonice: But how should women perform so wise and glorious an achievement, we women who dwell in the retirement of the household, clad in diaphanous garments of yellow silk and long flowing gowns, decked out with flowers and shod with dainty little slippers?

Lysistrata: Ah, but those are the very sheet-anchors of our salvation – those yellow tunics, those scents and slippers, those cosmetics and transparent robes.

Cleonice: How so, pray?

Lysistrata: There is not a man will wield a lance against another...

Cleonice: Quick, I will get me a yellow tunic from the dyer's.

Lysistrata: ...or want a shield.

Cleonice: I'll run and put on a flowing gown.

Lysistrata: ...or draw a sword.

Cleonice: I'll haste and buy a pair of slippers this instant.

Lysistrata: Now tell me, would not the women have done best to come?

Cleonice: Why, they should have flown here!

Lysistrata: Ah! My dear, you'll see that, like true Athenians, they will do everything too late... Why, there's not a woman come from the shore, not one from Salamis.

Cleonice: But I know for certain they embarked at daybreak.

Lysistrata: And the dames from Acharnae! Why, I thought they would have been the very first to arrive.

Cleonice: Theagenes' wife at any rate is sure to come; she has actually been to consult Hecate... But look! Here are some arrivals – and there are more behind. Ah! ha! Now what countrywomen may they be?

Lysistrata: They are from Anagyra.

Cleonice: Yes! Upon my word, 'tis a levy en masse of all the female population of Anagyra!

(Myrrhine enters, followed by other women.)

Myrrhine: Are we late, Lysistrata? Tell us, pray; what, not a word?

Lysistrata: I cannot say much for you, Myrrhine!

You have not bestirred yourself overmuch for an affair of such urgency.

Myrrhine: I could not find my girdle in the dark. However, if the matter is so pressing, here we are; so speak.

Cleonice: No, let's wait a moment more, till the women of Boeotia arrive and those from the Peloponnese.

Lysistrata: Yes, that is best... Ah! Here comes Lampito. (Lampito, a husky Spartan damsel, enters with three others, two from Boeotia and one from Corinth.) Good day, Lampito, dear friend from Lacedaemon. How well and handsome you look! What a rosy complexion! And how strong you seem; why, you could strangle a bull surely!

Lampito: Yes, indeed, I really think I could. It's because I do gymnastics and practise the bottom-kicking dance.

Cleonice: (opening Lampito's robe and baring her bosom) And what superb breasts!

Lampito: La! You are feeling me as if I were a beast for sacrifice.

Lysistrata: And this young woman, where is she from?

Lampito: She is a noble lady from Boeotia.

Lysistrata: Ah! my pretty Boeotian friend, you are as blooming as a garden.

Cleonice: (making another inspection) Yes, on my word! And her "garden" is so thoroughly weeded too!

Lysistrata: (pointing to the Corinthian) And who is this?

Lampito: 'Tis an honest woman, by my faith! She comes from Corinth.

Cleonice: Oh! Honest, no doubt then – as honesty goes at Corinth.

Lampito: But who has called together this council of women, pray?

Lysistrata: I have.

Lampito: Well then, tell us what you want of us.

Cleonice: Yes, please tell us! What is this very important business you wish to inform us about?

Lysistrata: I will tell you. But first answer me one question.

Cleonice: Anything you wish.

Lysistrata: Don't you feel sad and sorry because the fathers of your children are far away from you with the army? For I'll wager there is not one of you whose husband is not abroad at this moment.

Cleonice: Mine has been the last five months in Thrace – looking after Eucrates.

Myrrhine: It's seven long months since mine left for Pylos.

Lampito: As for mine, if he ever does return from service, he's no sooner home than he takes down his shield again and flies back to the wars.

Lysistrata: And not so much as the shadow of a lover! Since the day the Milesians betrayed us, I have never once seen an eight-inch gadget even, to be a leathern consolation to us poor widows... Now tell me, if I have discovered a means of ending the war, will you all second me?

Cleonice: Yes verily, by all the goddesses, I swear I will, though I have to put my gown in pawn, and drink the money the same day.

Myrrhine: And so will I, though I must be split in two like a flat-fish, and have half myself removed.

Lampito: And I too; why to secure peace, I would climb to the top of Mount Taygetus.

Lysistrata: Then I will out with it at last, my mighty secret! Oh! Sister women, if we would compel our husbands to make peace, we must refrain…

Cleonice: Refrain from what? Tell us, tell us!

Lysistrata: But will you do it?

Myrrhine: We will, we will, though we should die of it.

Lysistrata: We must refrain from the male altogether… Nay, why do you turn your backs on me? Where are you going? So, you bite your lips, and shake your heads, eh? Why these pale, sad looks? Why these tears? Come, will you do it – yes or no? Do you hesitate?

Cleonice: I will not do it, let the war go on.

Myrrhine: Nor will I; let the war go on.

Lysistrata: (to Myrrhine) And you say this, my pretty flat-fish, who declared just now they might split you in two?

Cleonice: Anything, anything but that! Bid me go through the fire, if you will, but to rob us of the sweetest thing in all the world, Lysistrata darling!

Lysistrata: (to Myrrhine) And you?

Myrrhine: Yes, I agree with the others; I too would sooner go through the fire.

Lysistrata: Oh, wanton, vicious sex! The poets have done well to make tragedies upon us; we are good for nothing then but love and lewdness! But you,

my dear, you from hardy Sparta, if you join me, all may yet be well; help me, second me, I beg you.

Lampito: 'Tis a hard thing, by the two goddesses it is! For a woman to sleep alone without ever a strong male in her bed. But there, peace must come first.

Lysistrata: Oh, my darling, my dearest, best friend, you are the only one deserving the name of woman!

Cleonice: But if – which the gods forbid – we do refrain altogether from what you say, should we get peace any sooner?

Lysistrata: Of course we should, by the goddesses twain! We need only sit indoors with painted cheeks, and meet our mates lightly clad in transparent gowns of Amorgos silk, and perfectly depilated; they will get their tools up and be wild to lie with us. That will be the time to refuse, and they will hasten to make peace, I am convinced of that!

Lampito: Yes, just as Menelaus, when he saw Helen's naked bosom, threw away his sword, they say.

Cleonice: But, oh dear, suppose our husbands go away and leave us?

Lysistrata: Then, as Pherecrates says, we must "flay a skinned dog", that's all.

Cleonice: Fiddlesticks! These proverbs are all idle talk… But if our husbands drag us by main force into the bedchamber?

Lysistrata: Hold on to the door posts.

"*M*" is a hump short when it comes to Ménage à trois, but let's not get carried away. First we have the straight up and down Missionary position. However, this letter is full of sensual movement, whether it's in Massage or Masturbation.

Missionary Position

This ever-popular classic suffered a bad press in the recent past, but it's now enjoying something of a comeback. One of its greatest advantages is that you can sustain it for an extended period of time, but it pays to maximize leverage by investing in a really firm yet comfortable mattress and preferably a bed with a footboard that he can press his feet against. In sex manuals, missionary scores badly on clitoral stimulation, but she can always reach down to do the necessary. Or, even better, following a main course of masturbation culminating in a clitoral coming, she can enjoy a mind-blowing dessert of vaginal orgasm with her man on top. His balls are also well within massaging distance, as is the perineum.

Manassé Photographic Studio The creative output of wife and husband Olga
and Adorján Wlassics – Hungarian émigrés who settled in Vienna in the 1920s – is
bewitchingly erotic, and their captivating imagery is the subject of a book by Monika
Faber entitled *Divas and Lovers*. Here we see reflected the glamorous world of film,
theatre, and cabaret in its extravagant heyday, in reaction to the austerity of the war years.
The Wlassics' speciality was creating unique portraits, complete with their trademark
"Manassé" signature, of the stars of stage and screen of the day, which the individuals
would use for promotion or publicity purposes. They also supplied various Austrian and
German magazines with elegant and tastefully titillating visuals to satisfy the public's
considerable appetite for a slice of the exotic pie. They employed elaborate lighting and
retouching techniques to construct an artificial, idealized setting and subject. Exaggerated
poses echoing the conventions of the silent movies, coupled with flamboyant hairstyling
and fashion, together with heavily symbolic props, all add to the wonderfully surreal
quality of the pictures.

Massage A range of novelty massage products are available on the market to
tickle you and your partner's fancy – "lickable" massage oil in a
number of fruity flavours, complete with various massage devices, or edible body finger
paints with which you can apply nerve-jangling designs to erogenous zones. Other subtly
teasing methods to experiment with include using a soft bristle brush or feather, or exploit
the textural effects of fur or silk. You could, on the other hand, get down to the business
properly and concoct your own aromatic massage oil. Blend one or more pure essential
oils, carefully following the guide to relative proportions, with a carrier oil such as sweet
almond (beware of nut allergy), grapeseed, or wheatgerm – the latter is good for the skin
into the bargain. Those fragrant oils with the best sensual credentials are jasmine, ylang-
ylang, and that essence of the flower-power era, patchouli.

Masturbation It is through masturbation that we first get to know how our bodies work sexually. All the diagrams and instructions in the world cannot show us the surest path to our own sexual satisfaction. If we can find and explore our individual pleasure points in our own time, free from outside pressures, we are then in a much better position to be able to direct our partners the right way from the outset, rather than leaving the matter to a potentially frustrating and damaging process of trial and error. Some people worry that continuing to masturbate while in a partnership is somehow being disloyal or might indicate to the other party that they are insufficiently satiated. But successful sexual activity tends to beget more of the same, so it's likely to be a positive not negative sign. Masturbating in front of each other can be a real winner, combining bespoke stimulation with the thrill of voyeurism.

Ménage à Trois What do Lord Nelson and the Hamiltons; Diane de Poitiers, Henry II, and Catherine de' Medici; Butch Cassidy, the Sundance Kid, and Etta Place; Anaïs Nin and Henry and June Miller have in common? The answer, *ménage à trois*! This term is quite often applied to group sex, or more specifically sex between three people, which is actually troilism. *Ménage à trois* is reserved for the more unusual (or so the uniformed might think, i.e. me) practice of three people living together or having a significant three-way relationship – it literally translates as "household of three". Yes, the phenomenon of the threesome has been rife down the ages, from Genesis to Ally McBeal, and this intriguing aspect of human history has been laid bare by a contemporary threesome – Barbara Foster, Michael Foster, and Letha Hadady in their book *Three In Love: Ménages à Trois From Ancient to Modern Times*. Here, the authors are at pains to stress the difference between (and they should know) the jealousy-fuelled wranglings of the eternal triangle and a consensual, three-way fellowship.

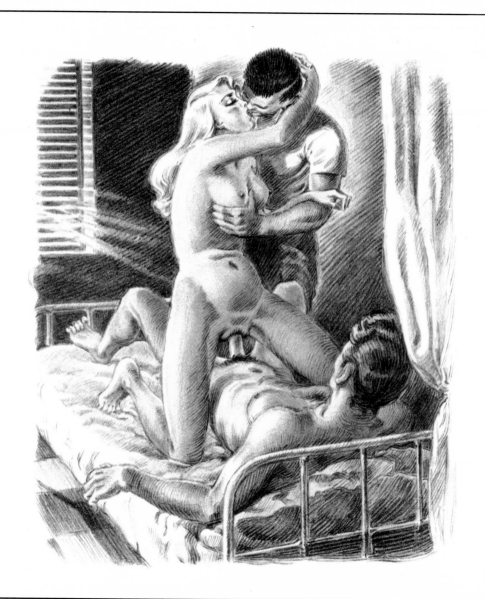

Anon. (20th Century)

Suzanne Ballivet (20th Century)

...*Mount* of *Pleasure*

Last night I dreamed my love
When sleep did overtake her.
It was a pretty, drowsy rogue;
She slept; I durst not wake her.

Her lips were like to coral red;
A thousand times I kissed 'um,
And a thousand more I might have stolen,
For she had never missed 'um.

Her crisped locks, like threads of gold,
Hung dangling o'er the pillows;
Great pity 'twas that one so fair
Should wear the rainbow-willow.

I folded down the holland sheet
A little below her belly,
But what I did you ne'er shall know,
Nor is it meet to tell ye.

Her belly's like to yonder hill –
Some call it Mount of Pleasure –
And underneath there springs a well
Which no man's depth can measure.

Anon (17th century)

Thomas Rowlandson (1756-1827)

M is for Catherine M

The Sexual Life of Catherine M

Catherine Millet

The following extract is taken from the autobiographical account of Parisian art critic Catherine Millet's sexual odyssey over a period of 30 years. Her celebration of heterosexuality in all its varieties is elegantly and coolly presented, without any hint of shame or guilt, in what has been described as "the most explicit book ever written by a woman".

I met Éric when I was 21, not before his existence had been "announced" to me; some mutual friends had frequently assured me that, given my predispositions, he was just right for me. After the holiday in Lyon had continued having group sex with Claude. With Éric, the regime intensified, not only because he took me to places where I could, as I have just shown, make myself available to an incalculable number of hands and penises, but more particularly because the sessions were well-organized. To my way of thinking, there has always been a clear-cut difference between, on the one hand, the more or less improvised situations which lead a group of people to redistribute themselves amongst the beds and sofas after a dinner, or which induce an excited gang of friends to drive around the porte Dauphine in their car until they make contact with other cars and all the passengers end up intermingling in a large apartment, and, on the other hand, the *soirées* curated by Éric and his friends. I preferred the inflexible sequence of the latter, and their exclusive goal: there was no rush and no tension: there were no outside factors (alcohol, demonstrative behaviour…) to impede the flow mechanics of bodies. Their comings and goings never strayed from their insect-like determination.

Victor's birthday parties impressed me the most. At the entrance to his property there were guards with dogs, talking into walkie-talkies, and I was intimidated by the crowds of people. Some women had dressed for the occasion, they wore transparent blouses or dresses, I was envious of them, and as people arrived and met up, sipping their champagne, I stood to one side. In fact, I only really relaxed once I had removed my dress or my trousers. My true clothing was my nudity, which shielded me.

I was amused by the architecture of the place because it was similar to the décor of a then very fashionable boutique on the boulevard Saint-Germain, called the "Gaminerie". It was, on a larger scale than the boutique, a cave, with its attendant cells, fashioned in white stucco. This "grotto" was underground and its only source of light came from the bottom of a swimming pool on the floor above. Through a pane of glass which formed a sort of vast television screen, we could see the succession of bodies diving in from the upper floor. I am describing a place in which I have never moved through a great deal. The scale of things had changed around me, but my situation was not very different from what it had been the first time, with my friends in Lyon. Éric would settle me on a bed or a sofa in one of the alcoves, respecting some vague custom by taking the initiative to undress me and put me on display. He might start to rub me and to kiss me but then would immediately hand me over to others. I would almost always stay on my back, perhaps because the other most common position, in which the woman actively straddles the man's pelvis, is less adapted to intervention from several participants and, anyway, implies a more personal relationship between the partners. On my back, I could be stroked by several men while one of them, rearing up to make room and see what he was doing, would get going in my vagina. I was tugged and nibbled in several places at once; one hand rubbing insistently round the available part of my pubis, another one skimming broadly across my entire torso or choosing to provoke my nipples…More than the penetrations, I took pleasure in caressing, and in particular when it was a penis that was trailed over the entire surface of my face or a glans that rubbed against my breasts. I liked to catch one in my mouth as it passed by, running my lips up and down it while another came and begged attention on the other side of my outstretched neck, before turning my head to take the newcomer. Or having one in my mouth and one in my hand. My body opened up more under the effects of this kind of stroking, which was relatively brief and could be renewed again and again, than in penetration itself. On that subject, what I remember most is the stiffness between my legs after being pinioned sometimes for four hours, especially as many men tend to keep the woman's thighs spread well apart, to make the most of the view and to penetrate further.

When I was left to rest, I would become aware that my vagina was gorged. It was a pleasure feeling its walls stiffened, heavy, slightly painful, in their own way bearing the imprint of all the members that had touched base there.

The position of the active spider in the middle of her web suited me well. Once – and this was not at Victor's house but in a sauna at the place Clichy – I hardly left the depths of a big armchair the whole evening, even though there was a huge bed in the middle of the room. With my head on a level with the dicks that made themselves available, I could suck at one while, with my hands on the arm rests, I jerked off two more at the same time. My legs were lifted up very high and, one after another, those who had become sufficiently aroused followed through in my cunt.

I sweat very little but sometimes I was drenched in my partners' sweat. There would also be threads of sperm that dried along the tops of my thighs, sometimes on my breasts or my face, even in my hair, and men who are into orgies really like shooting their load in a cunt that's already lined with cum. From time to time, on the pretext of going to the toilet, I would manage to extricate myself from the group and go to wash. Victor's house had a bathroom with a bluish light which was clear enough without being violent. A mirror took up the entire wall above the bath, and the deep, hazy image it reflected softened the atmosphere still further. I saw my body in it, and was amazed to see that it was smaller, slimmer than it had felt a few moments earlier. In there, more gentle exchanges took place. There was always someone there to compliment me on my olive skin or on the *savoir faire* I demonstrated with my mouth – very different as when, buried under bodies, I could hear, as if from a long way away, a conversation about myself, rather like a sleeping patient making out the doctor's and the interns' comments as they made their rounds of the beds.

A jet of water on my open, replete pussy. But few were the times when a man who had also come there for a pause did not make the most of the moment when I squatted over the bidet to jiggle his softened but always willing dick against my lips. And quite often, I would stand and put my hands on the washbasin, offering my vulva to increasingly firm pressure from an organ that eventually managed to deliver a few thrusts. One of my favourite delights is the pleasure given by an organ that slips between the labia and then affirms itself there, progressively separating them, before burying itself in what I have had plenty of time to establish as an eagerly accommodating space.

"N" may look like an evenly balanced sort of letter, but appearances can be deceptive — it doesn't do anything by halves. Take the all-consuming love of sex in Nymphomania and the all-conquering love of self in Narcissism. And then all is revealed in Nudity, just to prove that Naughty can be Nice.

Narcissism This term derives from the ancient Greek myth in which the handsome young Narcissus rejects the amorous advances of the nymph Echo, thus inviting the wrath of the gods, or the goddess Nemesis in this case, who leaves him to fall in love with his own reflection in the water. In fact, his final demise comes when he falls into the water and drowns while trying to kiss himself. But all is not lost – on the point of death, Nemesis turns him into the flower Narcissus that we all know and love. The sexual narcissist may well feed his (reputedly more likely) or her insatiable appetite for adoration and admiration by devouring (don't think Hannibal the Cannibal – not literally) sexual partners, who are regarded merely as conquests and as such proof of his/her continued superiority.

Nin, Anaïs The work of this French-born writer captured the spirit of a generation of women in the '70s – somewhat after the event. The snowball of her fame began to build when the first volume of her diary (1931–1934) finally saw the light of day in 1966, and was received as a lyrical, philosophical, and candid charting of a thoroughly modern woman's voyage of self-discovery. Trouble, however, brewed at a later date when it was discovered that Nin had not been telling the whole truth. Her economy with reality was in an attempt to preserve relationships and reputations, since Nin had been engaged in an illicit affair with Henry Miller during the period of the diary. But controversial renown didn't end there. Nin's hitherto unpublished erotica – mostly contained within two collections, *Delta of Venus* and *Little Birds* – was brought under the spotlight posthumously in the late '70s. Now considered by many to be some of the best erotic writing of modern times, Nin had written the stories in the '40s out of financial necessity for an anonymous client. Despite the mixed reception, *Delta of Venus* reputedly sold approaching a million copies in paperback in two years.

Nymphomania Historically, certainly in the dark age of the Victorians, any overt sign of sexual desire in a woman was seen either as a disease or a psychological disorder – even a plain old orgasm was viewed as "hysteria". Oddly, reading novels seems to have figured highly as the root cause of this shameful affliction. Against this unenlightened backdrop, we have the schoolboy stereotyping of the in-your-dreams "nympho", which also manages to leave a bad taste of derogatoriness. Being deemed "over-sexed" has to be an arbitrary judgement because who can say how much sex is too much? However, the clinical condition is specifically defined by an overwhelming compulsion for sex, the consequences of which are genuinely distressing and harmful to the individual.

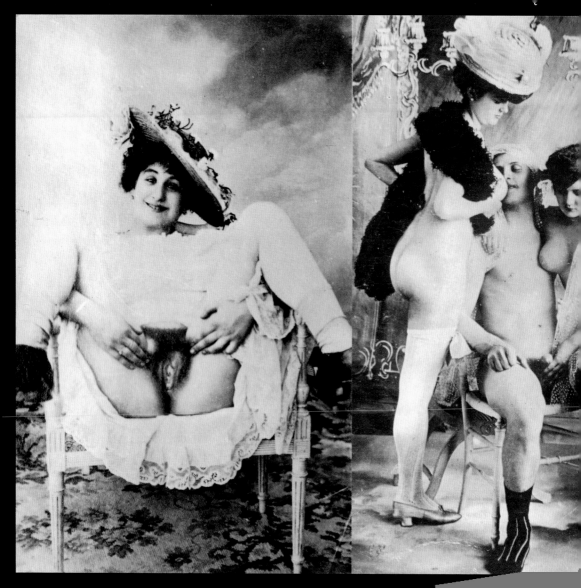

*She Lay All **Naked***

She lay all **naked** in her bed,
And I myself lay by;
No veil but curtains about her spread,
No covering but I:
Her head upon her shoulders seeks
To hang in careless wise,
And full of blushes were her cheeks,
And of wishes were her eyes.

Her blood still fresh into her face,
As on a message came,
To say that in another place
It meant another game;
Her cherry lip moist, plump, and fair,
Millions of kisses crown,
Which ripe and uncropped dangled there,
And weigh the branches down.

Her breasts, that welled so plump and high
Bred pleasant pain in me,
For all the world I do defy
The like felicity;
Her thighs and belly, soft and fair,
To me were only shown:
To have seen such meat, and not to have eat,
Would have angered any stone.

Her knees lay upward gently bent,
And all lay hollow under,
As if on easy terms, they meant
To fall unforced asunder;
Just so the Cyprian Queen did lie,
Expecting in her bower;
When too long stay had kept the boy
Beyond his promised hour.

"Dull clown," quoth she, "why dost delay
Such proffered bliss to take?
Canst thou find out no other way
Similitudes to make?"
Mad with delight I thundering
Throw my arms about her,
But pox upon't t'was but a dream.
And so I lay without her.

Anon (17th century)

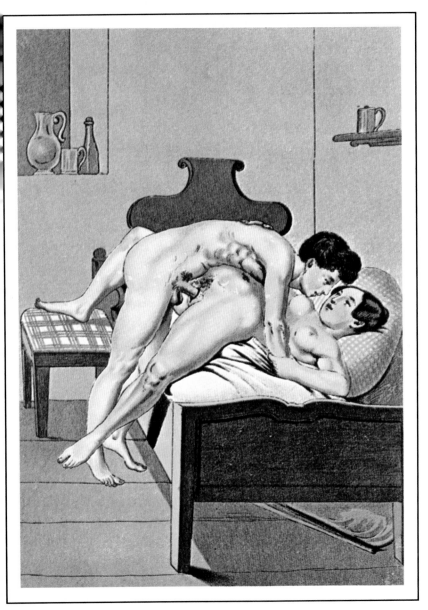

Peter Fendi (1796–1842)

N is for Names

Sundry names given to the sexual organs of women

Sheik Nefzawi

From *The Perfumed Garden*

El keuss (the vulva) – This word serves as the name of a young woman's vulva in particular. Such a vulva is very plump and round in every direction, with long lips, grand slit, the edges well divided and symmetrical and rounded; it is soft, seductive, perfect throughout. It is the most pleasant and no doubt the best of all the different sorts. It is warm, tight and dry.

El kehmoune (the voluptuous) – The name given to the vulva of a young virgin.

El ass (the primitive) – This is a name applicable to every kind of vulva.

El zerzour (the starling) – The vulva of a very young girl, or, as others pretend, of a brunette.

El cheukk (the chink) – The vulva of a bony, lean woman. It is like a chink in a wall, with not a vestige of flesh. May God keep us from it!

Abou tertour (the crested one) – It is the name given to a vulva furnished with a red comb, like that of a cock, which rises at the moment of enjoyment.

Abou khochime (the snub-nose) – Is a vulva with thin lips and a small tongue.

El gueunfond (the hedgehog) – The vulva of the old, decrepit woman, dried up with age and with bristly hail.

El sakouti (the silent one) – This name has been given to the vulva that is noiseless. The member may enter it a hundred times a day but it will not say a word, and will be content to look on without a murmur.

El deukkak (the crusher) – So called from its crushing movements upon the member. It generally begins to push the member, directly it enters, to the right and to the left, and to grip it with the matrix, and would, if it could, absorb also the two testicles.

El tseguil (the importunate) – This is the vulva which is never tired of taking in the member. This latter might pass a hundred nights with it, and still that vulva would not be sated. Luckily it is a rarity, and only found in a small number of women, who are wild with passion, all on fire, and in flame.

El taleb (the yearning one) – This vagina is met with in a few women only. With some it is natural; with others it becomes what it is by long abstinence. It is burning for a member, and, having got one in its embrace, it refuses to part with it until its fire is completely extinguished.

El hacene (the beautiful) – This is the vulva which is white, plump, in form vaulted like a dome, firm, and without any deformity. You cannot take your eyes off it, and to look at it changes a feeble erection into a strong one.

El neuffakh (the swelling one) – So called because a torpid member coming near it, and rubbing its head against it a few times, at once swells and stands upright. To the woman who has such a one it procures excessive pleasure, for, at the moment of the crisis, it opens and shuts convulsively, like the vulva of a mare.

Abou djebaha (one with a projection) – Some women have this sort of vulva, which is very large, with a pubis prominent like a projecting, fleshy forehead.

El ouasâ (the vast one) – A vulva surrounded by a very large pubis. Women of this build are said to be of large vagina, because, although on the approach of the member it appears impenetrable, as soon as it feels the friction of the glans against its centre it opens wide at once.

El aride (the large one) – This is the vulva which is as wide as it is long; that is to say, fully developed all round, from side to side, and from the pubis to the perineum. It is the most beautiful to look upon.

Abou belâoum (the glutton) – The vulva with a vast capacity for swallowing. If such a vulva has not been able to get coitus for some time it fairly engulfs the member that then comes near it.

El mokâour (the bottomless) – This is the vagina of indefinite length, having, in consequence, the matrix lying very far back. It requires a member of the largest dimensions; any other could not succeed in rousing its amorous sensibilities.

Abou cheufrine (the two-lipped) – This name is given to the amply developed vagina of an excessively stout woman. Also to the vagina the lips of which having become flaccid, owing to weakness, are long and pendulous.

Abou âungra (the humpbacked) – This vulva has the mount of Venus prominent and hard, standing out like the hump on the back of the camel. May God let us enjoy such a vulva! Amen!

El rorbal (the sieve) – This vulva on receiving a member seems to sift it all over, below, right and left, fore and aft, until the moment of pleasure arrives.

El hezzaz (the restless) – When this vagina has received the member it begins to move violently and without interruption until the member touches the matrix, and then knows no repose till it has hastened on the enjoyment and finished its world.

El lezzaz (the unionist) – The vagina which, having taken in the member, clings to it and pushes itself forward upon it so closely that, if the thing were possible, it would enfold the two testicles.

El moudd (the accommodating) – This name is applied to the vagina of a woman who has felt for a long time an ardent wish for coition. In rapture with the member it sees, it is glad to second its movements of come and go. Whatever place inside of it the member wants to explore, this vulva will make him welcome to.

El mouâine (the assistant) – This vulva is thus named because it assists the member to go in and out, to go up and down, in short, in all its movements. By this aid the ejaculation is facilitated, and the enjoyment heightened.

El meusboul (the long one) – This name

pplies only to some vulvas; everyone knows hat vulvas are far from being all of the same conformation and aspect. This vulva extends rom the pubis to the anus. It lengthens out when the woman is lying down or standing, and contracts when she is sitting, differing in his respect from the vulva of a round shape.

El molki (the duellist) – This is the vulva which, on the introduction of a member, executes the movement of coming and going, pushes itself upon it for fear of its retiring before the pleasure arrives. The vulva and the member resemble thus two skilful duellists, each time that one of them rushes its antagonist, the latter opposes its shield to parry the blow and repulse the assault. The member represents the sword, and the matrix the shield, and, assuredly, it is a fine fight! I should like thus to fight without stopping to the day of my death.

El harrab (the fugitive) – The vagina which, being very tight and short, is hurt by the penetration of a very large and soft member; it tries to escape to the right and left. It is thus, people say, like the vagina of most virgins.

El sabeur (the resigned) – This is the vulva which, having admitted the member, submits patiently to all its whims, and movements. It is also said that this vulva is strong enough to suffer resignedly the most violent and prolonged coitus. This kind of vagina is found in women of a glowing temperament.

El mouseuffah (the barred one) – This kind of vagina is not often met with. The defect which distinguished it is sometimes natural, sometimes it is the result of an unskilfully executed operation of circumcision upon the woman. It can happen that the operator makes a false move with his instrument and injures the two lips, or even only one of them. In healing there forms a thick scar, which bars the passage, and in order to make the vagina accessible to the member, a surgical operation and the use of the bistouri will have to be resorted to.

El merour (the deep one) – The vagina which always has the mouth open, and the bottom of which is beyond sight. The longest members only can reach it.

El âddad (the biter) – The vulva which, when the member has got into it and is burning with passion, opens and shuts again upon the same fiercely. It is chiefly when the ejaculation is coming that the man feels the head of his member bitten by the mouth of the matrix.

El meusass (the sucker) – This is a vagina which in its amorous heat in consequence of voluptuous toyings, or of long abstinence, begins to suck the member which has entered it so forcibly as to deprive it of all its sperm, dealing with it as a child drawing on the breast of the mother.

It's no wonder that "O" is an opulently erotic letter, with its orifice-like shape. So here we can indulge ourselves in an Orgy of sex, enjoying Orgasm along the way and taking a furtive peek at the "dirty books" of the Olympia Press, including the Story of O.

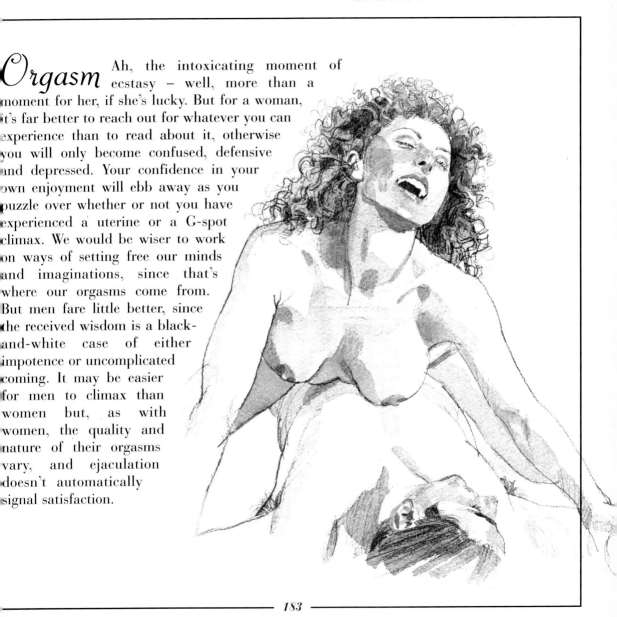

Orgasm

Ah, the intoxicating moment of ecstasy – well, more than a moment for her, if she's lucky. But for a woman, it's far better to reach out for whatever you can experience than to read about it, otherwise you will only become confused, defensive and depressed. Your confidence in your own enjoyment will ebb away as you puzzle over whether or not you have experienced a uterine or a G-spot climax. We would be wiser to work on ways of setting free our minds and imaginations, since that's where our orgasms come from. But men fare little better, since the received wisdom is a black-and-white case of either impotence or uncomplicated coming. It may be easier for men to climax than women but, as with women, the quality and nature of their orgasms vary, and ejaculation doesn't automatically signal satisfaction.

Oculophilia This relates to a fundamental of human non-verbal communication. It means sexual excitement induced by the eyes of another. Eye contact is a crucial aspect of courtship, even though the signals may vary according to different cultures. Common to most is the lowering of the eyes as a sign of submission. In the Western world, the holding of a gaze is the signal of sexual interest, but there are also unconscious indicators of attraction. Certain sex hormones will increase the diameter of a woman's pupils by up to 30 per cent, which can have a dynamic, albeit subliminal, effect on men. In Victorian times, women exploited this effect by artificially enlarging their pupils with a drug derived from deadly nightshade.

Olympia Press In censorship-lax Paris in the early 1930s an English dandy, "booklegger", and writer of saucy stories, Jack Kahane, who had fading health and few resources, founded the Obelisk Press with the intention of publishing challenging work by writers who would otherwise be "gagged" on the back of his own commercial potboilers. This sexual and expression freedom-fighter brought into print works by such luminaries as James Joyce, Henry Miller, Lawrence Durrell, Anaïs Nin, and Cyril Connolly. After Kahane's sudden death in 1939, his son, Maurice Girodias, took up the baton and established the Olympia Press in the '50s. The proposed formula of his enterprise echoed that of his father's – a steady stream of salacious material would generate the cash to fund groundbreaking works. So, Girodias and his cohort of young writers and translators set to and produced a series of "dirty books" under the banner of the Traveller's Companion, bound between distinctive yet discreet green covers. Girodias ensured that the English language "DBs" found their way to all corners of the globe, often traded by US servicemen as contraband. All this industry and cunning did indeed pay off, in the form of such literary landmarks as J. P. Donleavy's *The Ginger Man*, Pauline Réage's *The Story of O*, William Burroughs' *Naked Lunch*, Terry Southern and Mason Hoffenberg's *Candy*, as well as works by Samuel Beckett and Miller.

Onanism This nowadays rather obscure term was used, particularly in the 18th century, to denote our dear friend masturbation. It all goes back to the sorry tale of Onan in Genesis Chapter 38: "So when Onan went in to his brother's wife he spilled the seed on the ground, lest he give offspring to his brother. And what he did was displeasing in the sight of the Lord, and he slew him also." According to the prevailing levirate law of the Old Testament, Onan, after the death of his brother Er, was duty-bound to give his sister-in-law, Tamar, a child. However, because the resulting issue would have been deemed his brother's rather than his, he did the fatal semen-spilling. And this is where there has been a divergence of interpretation over the intervening centuries. Was Onan's sin the fact that he masturbated and therefore enjoyed sex in negation of its proper purpose, i.e. procreation, or, as is now generally believed, did he actually practice coitus interruptus, and in that way violated the levirate matrimonial laws? Either way, the wickedly witty Dorothy Parker paid homage to this Biblical morality tale by naming her pet parrot after Onan because, as she explained, he too spilled his seed on the ground.

Orgy Orgy is a suitably opulent term for group sex with attitude, as exemplified by the legendary excesses of the Classical world. However, what we tend to forget from our modern perspective is that it all went on in the name of religion; in other words, they just got a little carried away. The festivals of Demeter and Dionysus were to blame in the case of the Greeks. But the Romans in general, and Caligula in particular, made the orgy their own. One wonders, though, whether these events did in fact live up to their reputation of mythical proportions on the sexual front, given the amount of booze that was sunk – sometimes resulting in death. But the excessive drinking was as nothing compared to the drug-taking, which featured the highly toxic hemlock. In more recent times, May Day rituals signalled the OK for much frolicking around the phallic May pole – and more. With the customary codes of marriage suspended for the month, indiscriminate sex was naturally on the agenda.

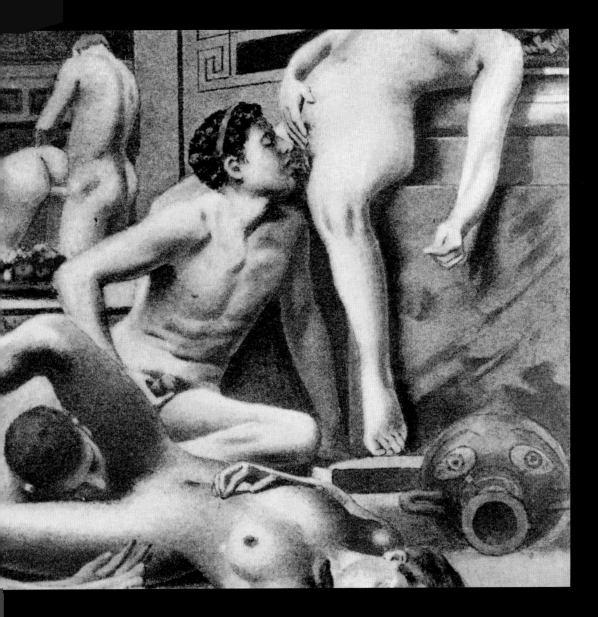

Oh – I can't bear it...

Be quiet, Sir! Begone, I say!
Lord bless us! How you romp and tear!
There!
I swear!
Now you left my bosom bare!
I do not like such boisterous play,
So take that saucy hard away –
Why now, you're ruder than before!
Nay, I'll be hanged if I comply –
Fie!
I'll cry!
***Oh** – I can't bear it – I shall die!*
I vow I'll never see you more!
But – are you sure you've shut the door?

Anon

Peter Fendi (1796–1842)

O is for Outdoor Sex

Sport Amongst The She-Noodles

Extract from *The Pearl*

My uncle's is a nice country residence, standing in large grounds of its own, and surrounded by small fields of arable and pasture land, interspersed by numerous interesting copses, through which run footpaths and shady walks, where you are not likely to meet anyone in a month. I shall not trouble my readers with the name of the locality, or they may go pleasure hunting for themselves.

Well, to go on, these cousins consisted of Annie, Sophie, and Polly, beside their brother Frank, who, at 19, was the eldest, the girls being, respectively, 18, 16, and 15. After dinner, the first day of my arrival, Paterfamilias and Mama indulged in a snooze in their armchairs, whilst us boys and girls (I was the same age as Frank) took a stroll in the grounds. I attached myself more particularly to cousin Annie, a finely developed blonde, with deep blue eyes, pouting red lips, and a full heaving bosom, which to me looked like a perfect volcano of smothered desires. I asked Annie to show me the improvements in the grounds before we went in to tea, saying to Frank, banteringly, "I suppose, old fellow, you're too lazy, and would prefer your sister taking me round?"

"I'm too comfortable. Lazy is an ugly word, Walter, but the fact is, Soph is just reading me a most interesting book, and I can't leave it," he replied. "Besides, sissie is quite as well or better qualified than I am to show off the grounds. I never notice anything."

"Come on, Annie," said I, taking her hand, "Frank is in love."

"No, I'm sure he never thinks of a girl, except his sisters," was the reply.

We were now out of earshot, in a shady walk, so I went on a little more freely. "But, surely you, coz, are in love, if he is not. I can tell it by your liquid eye and heaving bosom."

A scarlet flush shot over her features at my allusion to her finely moulded bosom, but it was evidently pleasing, and far from offensive, to judge by her playfully spoken: "Oh! Walter, for shame, sir!"

We were a good distance away by this time, and a convenient seat stood near, so throwing my arms around the blushing girl, I kissed her ruby lips, and drawing her to me, said, "Now, Annie, dear, I'm your cousin and old playfellow. I couldn't help kissing those beautiful lips, which I could always make free with when we were little boy and girl together; now you shall confess all before I let you go."

"But I've nothing to confess, sir."

"Do you never think of love, Annie? Look me in the face if you can say it's a stranger to your bosom," putting my hand familiarly round her neck till my right hand rested on one of the panting globes of her bosom.

She turned her face to mine, suffused as it was by a deeper blush than ever, as her dark blue eyes met mine, in a fearless search of my meaning. Instead of speaking in response to this mute appeal, I kissed her rapturously, sucking in the fragrance of her sweet breath till she fairly trembled with emotion.

It was just beginning to get dusk, my hands were caressing the white, firm flesh of her beautiful neck, slowly working their way a little lower towards the heaving bubbies. At last I whispered, "What a fine bust you have developed since I saw you last, dear Annie. You won't mind your cousin, will you, when everything used to be so free to each other? Besides, what harm can there be in it?"

She seemed on fire, a thrill of emotion seeming to shoot through both of us, and for several moments she lay almost motionless in my arms, with one hand resting on my thigh. Priapus was awake and ready for business, but she suddenly roused herself, saying, "We must never stop here. Let us walk round or they will suspect something."

"When shall we be alone again, darling? We must arrange that before we go in," I said quickly.

It was impossible to keep her on the seat, but as we walked on she said, musingly, "Tomorrow morning we might go for a stroll before lunch. Frank lies in bed, and my sisters are keeping house this week; I shall have to mind the tarts and pies next week."

I gave her another hug and a kiss, as I said, "How delightful that will be! What a dear, thoughtful girl you are, Annie."

"Mind, sir, how you behave tomorrow, not so much kissing, or I shan't take you for a second walk. Here, we are at the house."

Next morning was gloriously warm and fine. As soon as breakfast was over we started for our stroll, being particularly minded by Papa to be back in good time for luncheon.

I gradually drew out my beautiful cousin, till our conversation got exceedingly warm, the hot blood rushing in waves of crimson over her shamefaced visage.

"What a rude boy you have grown, Walter, since you were here last. I can't help blushing at the way you run on, sir!" she exclaimed.

"Annie, my darling," I replied. "What can be more pleasing than to talk of fun with pretty girls, of the beauties of their legs and bosoms, and all about them? How I should love to see your lovely calf at this moment, especially after the glimpses I have already had of a divine ankle," saying which I threw myself under a shady tree, close by a gate in a meadow, and drew the half-resisting girl down on the grass at my side, and kissed her passionately, as I murmured, "Oh! Annie, what is there worth living for like the sweets of love?"

Her lips met mine in a fiery embrace, but suddenly disengaging herself, her eyes cast down, and looking awfully abashed, she stammered out, "What is it? What do you mean, Walter?"

"Ah, coz dear, can you be so innocent? Feel here the dart of love all impatient to enter the mossy grotto between your thighs," I whispered, placing her hand upon my prick, which I had quickly let out of the restraining trousers. "How you sigh! Grasp it in your hand, dear. Is it possible that you do not understand what it is for?"

Her face was crimson to the roots of her hair as her hand grasped my tool, and her eyes seemed to start with terror at the sudden apparition of my cock. Taking advantage of her speechless confusion, my own hand, slipping under her clothes, soon had possession of her mount, and in spite of the nervous contraction of her thighs, the forefinger searched out the virgin clitoris.

"Ah! oh! Walter don't; what are you about?"

"It's all love, dear. Open your thighs a wee bit and see what pleasure my finger will make you experience," I again whispered, smothering her with renewed and luscious kisses and thrusting the velvet tip of my tongue between her lips.

"Oh! oh! You will hurt!" she seemed to sigh rather than speak, as her legs relaxed a little of their spasmodic contraction.

My lips continued glued to hers, our otherwise disengaged arms clasped each other closely round the waist, and her hand held my prick in a kind of convulsive grasp whilst my fingers were busy with clitoris and cunny. The only audible sound resembled a mixture of kisses and sighs, till all in a moment I felt her crack deluged with a warm, creamy spend whilst my own juice spurted over her hand and dress in loving sympathy.

In a short while we recovered our composure a little, and I then explained to her that the melting ecstasy she had just felt was only a slight foretaste of the joy I could give her by inserting my member in her cunny. My persuasive eloquence and the warmth of her desires soon overcame all maiden fears and scruples. Then, for fear of damaging her dress, or getting the green stain of the grass on the knees of my light trousers, I persuaded her to stand up by the gate and allow me to enter her from behind. She hid her face in her hands on the top rail of the gate as I slowly raised her dress. What glories were unfolded to view; my prick's stiffness was renewed in an instant at the sight of her delicious buttocks, so beautifully complemented by the white of her pretty drawers. As I opened them and exposed the flesh, I could see the lips of her plump, pouting cunny, deliciously feathered with soft, light down, her lovely legs, drawers, stockings, and pretty boots, making a *tout ensemble*, which as I write and describe them cause my prick to swell in my breeches – it was a most delicious sight. I knelt and kissed her bottom, slit, and everything my tongue could reach. Standing up, I prepared to take possession of the seat of love when, alas! a sudden shriek came from Annie, her clothes dropped, and all my arrangements were upset in a moment. A bull had unexpectedly appeared on the opposite side of the gate, and frightened my love by the sudden application of his cold, damp nose to her forehead. It is too much to contemplate that scene even now.

"$\mathcal{P}$" is another erect member of the alphabet, complete with bulbous head — in perfect shape for Phallus. But its bulge also denotes fecundity, as in Pregnant sex. We also explore $\mathcal{P}$'s dual claims on pain and pleasure in Piercing and PVC.

Pregnant Sex

We all know it's perfectly safe (unless she has a history of miscarriage) but do we feel happy doing it? It all depends on whether she feels OK physically – the first three months will be the trickiest time in this respect – and how positively she responds to the changes in her self-image. Some women really resent their swollen form and feel ugly and therefore unsexy. Others feel turned on by the increased voluptuousness of their breasts and belly and by the concept of fertility – it can be a time of heightened sexuality. Men can feel nervous about hurting the foetus or experience a sense of exclusion or alienation. Alternatively, he can feel sexually supercharged by this public manifestation of potency and will revel in his mate's fecundity. Spooning is the ideal antidote to that beached whale feeling, where he can lavish attention on her magnificent mammaries.

Perfumed Garden, The

Written in the 16th century by Sheik Umar ibn Muhammed al-Nefzawi in Arabia, as with the *Kama Sutra*, it was largely thanks to Sir Richard Burton that the book reached a wider public in the West. Burton's exclusive Kama Shastra Society published it in 1886 without reference to himself. Sadly, Burton died before he was able to complete work on a new translation directly from the Arabic, which would have included a previously omitted section on homosexuality. An added dimension to this book, as compared with the *Kama Sutra*, is that it features some 20 or more erotic stories. On the "technical" side, chapters include "Concerning the Causes of Impotence in Men" and "Of Things That Take Away the Bad Smell from the Armpits and Sexual Parts of Women and Contract the Latter", in addition to the customary contortionist sex positions. The chapter on "Prescriptions for Increasing the Dimensions of Small Members and for Making Them Splendid" is illuminating. The text suggests procuring and boiling an ass's member, macerating it in oil, and anointing the penis with the resultant fluid – as well as drinking it.

Piercing

Today pleasure is what piercing is all about, and that for some includes the masochistic high from the pain involved in the process – although some piercings are billed as being relatively painless. The most famous and one of the most popular piercings for men is the Prince Albert, where a ring enters the urethra and comes out behind the glans on the underside of the penis. Ironically, given the prevailing prudery of the age, this does apparently derive from the man himself, consort to Queen Vic, who reputedly wore what was known as a "dressing ring", by which the penis was strapped tightly to one side or the other – hence the traditional tailor's question: "On which side does sir dress?" This was done in the interests of minimizing the bulge in the fashionably tight trousers of the day. A popular piercing for women is vertically through the clitoral hood, where the jewellery hangs down to stimulate the clitoris.

Prostate The prostate – or prostrate, as some would have it – has of late gained something of a negative reputation, which is, in many ways, a blessing, since it has raised people's awareness of the potential cancer risk and therefore increased the chances of early detection and treatment. However, it also has the capacity to deliver untold pleasure, since it's also regarded as the male G-spot. But as with the female equivalent, some exploratory graft is required to locate it because you can't actually see it. Having said that, the perineum, which is basically the external area between the anus and the balls, roughly corresponds to the internal siting of the prostate, so some firm rubbing at the central midway point should, in turn, press the sex button. For direct stimulation, you will need to make your approach via the anus. Using plenty of lubricant, and a gradual mode of entry, insert your longest digit through the opening as far as it will go. Reach straight upwards and then crook the finger forward against the tissue and feel for something firmer, i.e. the walnut-sized gland. Don't give up in vain – it's definitely in there somewhere.

PVC For those who are devotees of fetish fashion, polyvinyl chloride, or PVC, is the alternative material of choice to the traditional rubber – that is, after leather of course. Its characteristic wet-look finish makes it as stimulating to look at as it is to wear. It's also rather more negotiable than latex in the getting on-and-off stakes, but that can spoil part of the fun for some. Other finishes are available, such as a more subtle satin effect or snakeskin-like texture for enhanced tactile interest. You can dress yourself entirely in the stuff, from corsets to chokers, or wallow in the wonder of PVC sheets. And it doesn't just come in regulation fetish black. But there is a potential rip in the PVCists' regalia. In response to reports of an increase in the incidence of infertility among those involved in the manufacture of PVC, the European Commission has been threatening to ban it. In which case, it could be back to basics and latex.

Vivant Denon (1747-1826)

...in the **Park**

Much wine had passed, with grave discourse
Of who fucks who and who does worse
(Such as you usually do hear
From those who diet at the Bear),
When I, who still take care to see
Drunkenness relieved by lechery,
Went out into St James's Park
To cool my head and fire my heart.
But though St James has th' honour on't
'Tis consecrate to prick and cunt.
There by a most incestuous birth,
Strange woods spring from the teeming earth;
For they relate how heretofore
When ancient Pict began to whore,
Deluded of his assignation
(Jilting it seems was then in fashion)
Poor pensive lover, in this place
Would frig upon his mother's face;
Where rows of mandrakes tall did rise
Whose lewd tops fucked the very skies.

Each imitative branch does twine
In some loved fold of Aretine,
And nightly now beneath their shade
Are buggeries, rapes, and incests made.
Unto this all-sin-sheltering grove
Whores of the bulk and the alcove,
Great ladies, chambermaids, and drudges,
The ragpicker, and heiress trudges.
Car-men, divines, great lords, and tailors,
Prentices, poets, pimps, and jailers,
Footmen, fine fops do here arrive
And here promiscuously they swive.

"Aretine" is a reference to the Italian writer Pietro Aretino
(see pages 80 and 210).

From "A Ramble in St James's Park",
John Wilmot, Earl of Rochester (1647–1680)

Louis André Berthommé-Saint-André (1905-1977)

P is for Painful Sex

Flogging a Dead Frog

Richard Smithson

Sadly the Marquis de Sade died in 1814, 22 years before Leopold von Sacher-Masoch was born. History was therefore deprived of a beautiful symbiotic relationship[1], although the fact that the former would have been 100 years old on the latter's fourth birthday makes it seem unlikely that the Marquis would have been able to administer the kicking that the Count so richly deserved.

Without wanting to sound too much like the hairy-chested hetero I so plainly am, I have never really warmed to Sacher-Masoch. Of course, we have all at some time wanted to be whipped like a dog at the feet of a woman dressed in furs – I know I have – but he does go on about it so. And it really doesn't seem to be any fun. In *Venus in Furs*, he describes a scene in which, when he was a child, his aunt entered the room in her fur-lined jacket with the cook, kitchen-maid, and cat[2]. Naturally, it all ends in tears (bound hand and foot...whipped by his evil aunt...blood...tears...etc) but the effect is a little spoiled by the rather plonking morals that he will insist on drawing the whole time[3]. "Now you understand the suprasensual fool! Under the lash of a beautiful woman my senses first realized the meaning of woman!" Yes, yes, yes, get on with it.

Not only that, but the whining little toad doesn't come once in all the interminable pages of his book – which, let me remind Mr So-Called Erotic Writer, is *supposed* to be all about sex[4]. It may be that he had the good sense to realize that if he came all over his wife's fur coat she would beat him to a pulp for real, and not stop when he gave the password either. (Of course, if you are the President of the USA you can come over any bloody clothing you like, and the silly girl will keep the stained garment as a souvenir. Can you imagine Sacher-Masoch sticking a cigar up Wanda?) Or perhaps I am missing the point. Perhaps it isn't about sex at all, any more than post-football communal baths are – just a healthy opportunity to get a lot of testosterone off your chest, and incidentally sit in a hot bath with your foot on your best friend's willy.

The Marquis de Sade is much easier to understand: harassed by his mother-in-law and imprisoned in the Bastille for most of his adult life[5], it is not surprising that his imagination ran riot. What is unforgivably sadistic was his fondness for amateur theatricals, which he indulged in to captive audiences at Charenton asylum[6]. De Sade (known to the French as "the Divine Marquis", which may only be in comparison with Edith Cresson) was simply a dirty old man writ large.

If he hadn't been French, I dare say he would have been forgotten by now, but it is no use pointing out to our Gallic cousins that *Justine* and *120 Days of Sodom* are the most unmentionable tripe; they dearly love a philosopher, and the fact that they can't understand a word he is saying doesn't prevent them from stopping Jacques Derrida in the street and offering to have his babies. No, no, the Divine Marquis was just off his rocker – as who wouldn't be after tossing himself off six times a day for three years.

What would the Marquis have done if he had

met the Count? Sacher-Masoch was fastidiously clean, and a natty dresser, and de Sade's coprophilia would have been very upsetting, especially in the days before dry-cleaning. On the other hand, even in his obese old age, the Marquis retained a certain dignity, grace, and elegance, whereas you just know that Leopold would have had absolutely no small-talk, and would get all clammy and agitated when a strapping *hausfrau* hove into view, especially if she was wearing a day-glo, fun-fur crop-top and bondage trousers.

What they would have had in common if they ever had met can only be a matter of speculation. (You don't say.) I like to think that the Count's father would have tried to do the best for his son, and asked the aging Marquis to stand as godfather if he ever got out of prison. Clearly, as the Marquis would have been 117 years old when von Sacher-Masoch came of age, physical intimacy (other than a palsied handshake) would have been out of the question; but it would be nice to think that the old man would have reflected that, since he could no longer bugger his grandson, the very least that he could do would be to send him a Valentine card with a picture of a young woman in a fur coat whipping a pallid young man with a drooping moustache [7] [8]. In exchange, the Count could offer his speckled and quavering buttocks for inspection, safe in the knowledge that no harm could come to them in that company.

The Emperor Heliogabalus offered a fortune to anyone who could invent a new vice[9], but the reward went unclaimed in his lifetime. How come France came up with sadism, and Germany with masochism? Why isn't there a seminal Estonian novel about a young man who sniffed women's bicycle seats[10], leading to a whole sub-culture of bicycle-seat sniffing, and an international Internet network of clandestine inhalers? What about an Englishman force-feeding his excrement to middle-aged women?[11] There must be a whole world of unusual practices waiting to twang the wires of a generation so jaded that the follollopy Charlie Dimmock is the last word in titillation.

Now that sadism has been replaced by fetishism, and masochism by Andrew Lloyd Webber, we need a new perversion for the new millennium. Something to get the juices flowing. Or not, as the case may be; I don't want to cramp your style. It shows the deplorable spinelessness of Cool Britannia that nowhere in the Millennium Dome was there the slightest hint of how we might be getting our jollies in the 21st century. De Sade was an innovator, but he couldn't have expected his particular practices to be the last word. He must be turning in his grave.

Notes

1. Similar, for example, to the pairing of William Tell with Saint Sebastian, or Tracy Emin with Blind Pew.

2. The cat plays no further part in the story.

3. So German.

4. His wife Wanda wrote a book of memoirs in which she said what a drag it was to have to dress up in a fur coat and beat the crap out of her recalcitrant spouse. It sounds a pretty cushy life to me. (Though curiously enough she doesn't seem to have come at all in the course of her marriage either.) She should think herself lucky she wasn't married to the Marquis de Sade. Or Gary Bushell.

5. He estimated that in the first three years of imprisonment he masturbated 6,600 times, i.e. six times a day: once before breakfast, once at elevenses, once at lunch, once in mid-afternoon, once just before dinner, and once with his bedtime cocoa.

6. The Charenton Asylum Players' 1790 production of *The Mikado*, with Madame Defarge, Charlotte Corday, and Robespierre as the Three Little Maids from School, had to be seen to be believed. "Strong ensemble playing was sadly let down by an interpolated scene in which Nanki-Poo tore off Yum-Yum's head and defecated down the hole in her neck." *Le Figaro.*

7. On Valentine's day in Wales it is traditional to present your love with a wooden spoon. Says it all really. Just another thing that Michael Douglas will have to get used to.

8. This sentence gives the unfortunate impression that she is using the moustache to whip him. Hang on, though, that's an idea...

9. "At Rome he did nothing but send out agents to search for those who had particularly large organs and bring them to the palace in order that he might enjoy their vigour."

10. For whom the technical word is a "snoob", after Arvo Snoeb, its author.

11. Ask Jeffrey Archer's publisher.

This article first appeared in The Erotic Review *(see page 319).*

"Q", with its highly attractive yet complex construction, is one of the quirkier characters of the Lexicon of Love. We see it helping aptly to describe the female pudenda in Quim, aiding the explanation of a curious sexual practice in Queening, and leading us into the esoteric arts of Quodoushka. But it also gives us a welcome Quickie.

Quim This is an appropriately graphic term for the female genitalia, or more particularly the vagina, probably more familiar to folk in the 17th and 18th centuries than now. There are innumerable names for women's privates as indeed there are for men's, with new ones being added to our "lexicon of lewd" with every generation. Many are unashamedly (and unimaginatively) crude – crack, cunt, gash, hole, slot, slash, slit, and snatch, for example. Without wishing to be over-precious, there are some more fetching terms. From the ancient East, we have the poetic jade gate, pavilion, or palace, or the cinnabar grotto, while the great American blues singer, Bessie Smith, sang of the seductive sugar bowl. Also on the food theme, we have honey pot, lunch box, and oyster. Playfully predatory are mantrap, manhole, and organ-grinder. Or how about yawn?

Tom Poulton (20th Century)

Queening This really is in-your-face sex, or, to be exact, on-your-face. This term denotes the sexual practice of a woman sitting on a man's head as if she were gracing a throne. The prime objective is for her to use her genitalia to smother him, in order to restrict his breathing – in other words, we've entered BD (bondage and domination) territory here, if not SM (sadomasochism). Breath-control techniques are employed to prolong the agony/ecstasy. Obviously, it is vital that some kind of non-verbal signal is agreed upon between participants in advance, so that he is allowed to come up for air when necessary. Known as "macrophiles", some people – in most cases men – are turned on by the notion of being dwarfed and overpowered by an over-sized individual, in terms of being sat on or crushed or suffocated by them, and with extreme prejudice, I might add.

Quodoushka The Quodoushka teachings, often termed Chuluaqui Quodoushka, derive from the Native American tradition of the Cherokee. "Chuluaqui" would seem to be something akin to the "chi", "ki", or "prana" of the ancient Eastern philosophies, i.e. an energy that is fundamental to life. "Quodoushka" is the sacred union of two life-force energies, which is greater than the sum of the two. These teachings have been brought to a contemporary audience by Swift Deer, a teacher and healer of Cherokee descent, and workshops are on offer to tutor those keen to partake of these ancient wisdoms. Emphasis is placed on exploring all the senses in a prelude to lovemaking – sight, smell, taste, and touch – as well as breathing exercises and balancing each other's energy centres, with reference to "chakras", again reminiscent of Tantric teachings. There are different types and levels of orgasm to be had, including a "Look, no hands" variety called the Firebreath Orgasm, achieved without the aid of physical contact with a partner nor direct stimulation of the genitals.

Sylvie Jones (Contemporary)

Sonnet Lussuriosi

As I can now feel such an impressive tool
That's opening up the edges of my **quim**
I wish I was nothing but quim
And that you were all tool.

If I was quim and you were tool
For a whole I'd sate my quim
While you would strip my quim
Of all pleasures wanted by a tool
So take the good wishes of this quim

You too. Take from this modest tool
The same good wishes. Lower the quim
And I will raise the tool.
Then on my tool
Go made with your quim
I will be all tool. You – all quim.

Pietro Aretino (1492–1556)

Peter Fendi (1796–1842)

Q is for Quirky Sex

Beatrice

From *Beatrice*. The Scarlet Library

I do not like old rooms that are brown with the smell of time.

The ceilings in my husband's house were too high. They ran away from me. In the night I would

reach up my hands but I could not touch them. When Edward asked me what I was doing I said

I was reaching my hands up to touch the sky. He did not understand. Were we too young together?

Once a week he would remove my night dress and make love to me. Sometimes I moved, sometimes I did not. Sometimes I spoke, sometimes I did not speak. I did not know the words to speak. We quarrelled. His stepmother would scold us. She could hear. In the large, high-ceilinged rooms voices carried as burnt paper flies, rising, tumbling, falling, drifting.

The doors were always half open. Sometimes – lying in bed as if upon a huge cloud – I would play with his prick, his cock, his pintle. Pintle. I do not like the "nt" in it. Sometimes I would turn and he would rub it against the groove in my bottom. I liked that. I lay with my nightgown up, my back to him, and had my dreams. The rubbing was nice. My cheeks squeezed tightly on his cock.

The night before I left we quarrelled. Our words floated about, bubble-floating. They escaped through the door. His stepmother netted them. She entered and spoke to us. The oil lamps were still lit.

"I will bring you wine – you must be happy," she said. Her nightgown was pale and filmy. I could see her breasts. Balloons.

I could see the dark blur of her pubis, her pubic hair, her wicked.

"Wine, yes 'twould be splendid," Edward said. He was pale and thin. Like his pintle. I had nursed it in my palm even while we quarrelled. It was the warm neck of a bird. I did not want it in my nest. I heard his stepmother speaking to the maid downstairs.

The maid was always up. There was clinking – bottle sounds, glasses sounds. We lay still, side by side. His stepmother returned and closed the door, bearing a tray. She poured wine. We sat up like people taking medicine.

"Angela, dear, lie down," Edward said. His father had remarried her when Edward was 14. During the past months then of his father's absence in India, she had encouraged him to use her Christian name. I judged her about 40. A woman in full bloom.

Wine trickled and spilled on the sheet as she got in. Edward was between us – between the betweening of us. The ceiling grew higher. The sounds of our drinking sounded. The wine was suitably chilled. My belly warmed it. We were people in a carriage, going nowhere. We indulged ourselves in chatter. The bottle emptied quickly.

"We must sleep, we must lie down," Angela said.

"I will stay with you until you sleep."

I heard her voice say that. The ceiling came down. It had never done that before. I passed my hand up into it and it was made of cloud. We lay down side by side on our backs. Our breathing came. There was warmth. Edward laid his hand on my thigh. He moved my nightgown up inch by inch. He touched. Into my fur, my nest, he touched. The lips were oily, soft. I did not move. His hand on the other side of him moved. I could feel the sheet fluttering there.

Our eyes were all open. I did not look but I knew. Soft, wet sounds. I tried not to move my bottom. Would the maid enter to remove the tray? Edward's fingertips found my button. I felt rich, forlorn, lost. My legs stretched down and widened. My toes moved. On the other side of him the sheet fluttered still.

Edward moved. His finger was oily with my oil. He moved on his hip and turned towards me. I felt the pronging of his prong. His hand cupped my nest.

"Kiss goodnight, Beatrice."

His voice was above me, yet far away – a husk blown on the wind. I moved my face sideways to his.

"Yes, kiss goodnight," Angela said.

Her voice was far away – a leaf floating on the sea. His mouth met mine. His charger quivered against my bared thigh. Fingers that were not my fingers ringed the stem of his cock. His finger entered me.

I moved not. Our mouths were pasted together, unmoving. I was running through meadows and my father was chasing me. My mother and my sister, Caroline, were laughing. I screeched. Their voices drifted away on to the far horizon and waved there like small flags.

Moving my hand I encountered Angela's hand – the rings upon her fingers that ringed around his cock. I moved my mouth away from Edward's and stared up at the ceiling. It had gone high, gone high again. Birds drifted through it. Edward's hand eased my thighs wider. I lay limp, moist in my moistness. The bed quivered as if an engine were running beneath it.

I found my voice.

"Kiss goodnight," I said. My mind was not blank. There was coloured paper in it. A kaleidoscope. I watched the swirling, the patterns. Would love come?

Edward turned. His knob burned in his turning against my thigh. His nightgown was fully raised. His lips fell upon Angela's. Her hand held his cock still. At first she lay motionless. The sheet moved, tremored, rippled up and down. In her breathings were the secrets of the passageways at night.

Edward groaned in his groaning. The meshing of their lips.

I heard their tongues. Voices.

"Edward – no, not now!"

They were speaking in ordinary speech.

"Oh, you bad boy!"

The sheet became tented. I felt the opening of her thighs – the warmth exuding from her thick-furred nest. Her bottom shifted, rucking the sheet, smack-bounce of flesh to flesh. Her knees bent. Between her thighs she encompassed him. Small wet sounds. Slithery sounds. I held my legs open. I was gone, lost.

They did not know me. The bed heaved, shook. I turned my head. I looked as one looks along a beach at other people.

Did I know them?

Her nipples stood like tiny candles in brown saucers, laved by Edward's tongue. Her hands gripped his shoulders. Her eyes and lips were closed as if she were communing. Between her thighs his loins worked with febrile jerkings. Tiny squishing sounds. Her bottom began to move, jerking to his jerks.

Expressionless I moved the sheet down with my foot. It wrinkled, crinkled, slid away, betraying the curves of her calves. His mouth buried her mouth beneath his mouth. Her hands clawed his back. Their movements became more frenetic. The pale pistoning of his pintle cock. Moaning in the night. Bliss of it. Was there bliss of it?

I wanted to be held down. I wanted a straw to chew or a piece of long sweet grass whose root is white. Angela was panting. It was a rough sound. The squelching of his indriving, outsucking. His balls smacked her bottom. The sound pleased me. Through their puffing cheeks the working of their tongues.

"Ah! dearest, let me come!"

Edward raised himself on forearms, loins flashing. Her hands clutched his arms. I was looking. Sideways along a cloud, a beach. The lamps were lit still. Had they forgotten the lamps?

"Oh, Edward!"

Kiss goodnight.

He collapsed, he shuddered, in his quivering quivered. Her calves rose and gripped his buttocks. A final thrust, indriven to the root. He seeped in his seeping, his jetting done. Like balloons bereft of air they collapsed. They were quiet. I could hear the ceiling. The floor creaked. Was the bed coming undone?

Edward rolled between us and was quiet. The night was done. The limp worm of his penis-pole lolled wet against my thigh. Sticky. It oozed. It was too small now for my nest.

In the night he stirred and mounted me. Drowsy in coils of sleep I did not resist. The oil lamps flickered low. Did she watch? From moment to moment I jerked my bottom in long memories of knowing. I wore drawers in my dreams. My bottom was being smacked. It was being smacked because there was a cock in me. In our soft threshings my legs spread. My ankle touched hers. She did not stir. Our feet rubbed gently together. Our toes were intimate.

Edward worked his work upon me and was done. The spurtings came in long, strong trills of warmth. Warm, wet sperm trickled down my thighs. I lay inert. I had not come. He had not pleasured me. My nipples were untouched.

In the morning I left.

This is the letter that headed up the sexual Revolution, so there's clearly nothing retiring about "R" — it's basically in to everything. After Rear entry we take a look at some ancient and bizarre Rituals and end up in Rubber.

Rear Entry

This is another wonderfully spontaneous, raunchy coupling, best undertaken almost fully clothed. It's the notion of easy access, anywhere, any place, that provides the extra thrill. There is also something innately erotic in the sudden explosion of raw sexual energy in the context of the workaday environment with its respectable air of normality – in this instance at the very hub of routine domestic activity. She, panty-less or wearing the flimsiest G-string, lifts her skirt as her wanton lust grips her, bends over something solid to hand (kitchen sink, table, desk), spreads her legs, and flaunts her genitalia. Penetration is swift as he firmly grasps her hips, and she steadies herself against and over the chosen item of furniture while his groin pounds into her protruding buttocks. This scenario is a fantasy favourite, in case you don't quite get round to it in reality – one that's almost guaranteed to ignite most people's sexual fire, unless, of course, you have an obsession about the pristine state of your kitchen.

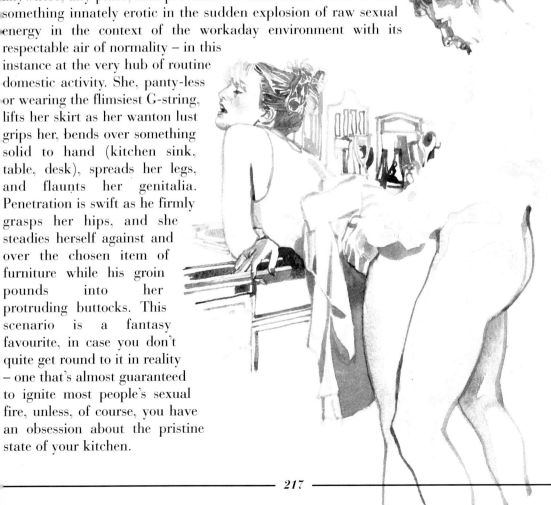

Restraints Restraints used in BD and SM sex play take many different forms, and a wide range of bespoke bondage accessories is readily available from mail-order catalogues or the Internet. These include various buckled leather ankle or wrist cuffs and chokers with chain attachments that inter-link the bindings behind the back. Rubber restraints are surprisingly comfortable, and a PVC bondage tape is particularly user-friendly when it comes to binding up your partner. Some restraints, however, are only used "symbolically" in that they are largely ineffectual in physically holding the individual in place. These might be a loosely tied silk scarf or tie, or a ribbon tied in a bow. But for those seeking something even more aesthetic, how about restraining in traditional Oriental style? In the book *The Seductive Art of Japanese Bondage* by Midori, we see how the elaborate binding and tying of rope, by which the "submissive" is suspended in midair, can produce a vision of serenely sensual beauty. But, this is the art of the highly skilled rope-masters; rope bindings in the hands of the amateur need to be rather less ambitious for safety.

Ritual Sex We're back to religion here. Some very shocking "sexual" acts of the most extreme sadomasochistic variety have been performed in the name of religious rites, including castration, impaling, burning, amputation, and cannibalism, with zoophilia (sex with animals) sometimes added to the unholy brew. However, ancient ceremonial sex wasn't always that nasty. Take Innana, for instance, who was worshipped as the Goddess of Sumeria back in 3500 BC. Among her many titles was Queen of the Earth and ergo Goddess of Fertility, which particularly related to the life-sustaining crops of the day. So, to ensure a successful harvest, Innana's mythical wedding to Dumuzi at the Spring Equinox was honoured each year in the temples of the land by the Sacred Marriage – a ritual union between a High Priestess and a Priest-King. Today, Beltane (May Day) is the favoured time to perform Sex Magick. Rituals feature synchronized breathing, visualization, rhythmic stroking, and, again, sacred union.

Rubber This is the second skin of choice for many fetishists of the material world. Its origins as a focus of fetish fancy bring a whole new meaning to the "man in the mac" stereotype. Passion for the humble mackintosh of rain-lashed England fame, with its hallmark rubber exterior, was the driving force behind the foundation of one of the earliest-known fetishist organizations, the Mackintosh Society. Thankfully, rubber comes in rather more chicly sleek forms these days – in fact, the age of designer latex has now arrived, with its figure-hugging and -enhancing qualities even being recognized beyond the fetish fellowship in the mainstream fashion industry. Wearers extol the sensual virtues of the wet and warm sensations that latex has to offer, and of course its restrictive qualities are definitely part of the charm. But how the hell do you get it on, let alone off? Purists swear by the liberal use of talcum powder, but there are now products specially designed to do the job with ease, together with sprays for maintaining that "just-buffed" look. If you feel the desire to parade your raunchy rubberwear in public, the famous Skin Two Rubber Ball in London, reputedly the world's largest fetish knees-up, is just the place for it.

Rumpy-pumpy This rather quaint term for the sexual act is quintessentially English – the saucy seaside postcard side of sex, brimming over with bawdy humour in a barmaid's bosom kind of way. In the same jocular, sing-along vein is rumpty-tumpty, hanky-panky, and jiggery-pokery. Rather more direct and descriptive are the "-ing" terms – balling, banging, boning, and bonking; humping and hosing; ploughing, plumbing, poking, and porking; and tooling. It all sounds very workmanlike. Maybe it's preferable to get one's rocks off, get one's end away, get one's pole polished, or, indeed, one's leather stretched, which is always nice. If, on the other hand, you've gone once around the park, and then gone for the home run, and scored, will you still have the energy for a session of making whoopee? After all that, you might feel like settling for a little of the old in and out, or a bit of nooky.

Roving hands...

Come, Madam, come, all rest my powers defy,
Until I labour, I in labour lie.
The foe oft-times, having the foe in sight,
Is tired with standing, though they never fight.
Off with that girdle, like heaven's zone glistering
But a far fairer world encompassing.
Unpin that spangled breast-plate, which you wear
That the'eyes of busy fools may be stopped there:
Unlace yourself, for that harmonious chime
Tells me from you that now 'tis your bed time
Off with that happy busk, whom I envy
That still can be, and still can stand so nigh.
Your gown's going off such beauteous state reveals
As when from flowery meads th'hills shadow steals.
Off with your wiry coronet and show
The hairy diadem which on you doth grow.
Off with those shoes: and then safely tread
In this love's hallowed temple, this soft bed.

In such white robes heaven's angels used to be
Received by men; thou Angel bring'st with thee
A heaven like Mahomet's Paradise; and though
Ill spirits walk in white, we easily know
By this these Angels from an evil sprite:
They set out hairs, but these the flesh upright.

Licence my **roving hands**, and let them go
Behind, before, above, between, below.
Oh my America, my new found land,
My kingdom, safeliest when with one man manned,
My mine of precious stones, my Empery,
How blessed am I in this discovering thee.
To enter in these bonds is to be free,
Then where my hand is set my seal shall be.

From "To His Mistress Going to Bed", John Donne (c. 1572–1631)

The Fumbler, Thomas Rowlandson (1756–1827)

R is for Religious Sex

Nuns In Their Twats

Dr Christopher Hart

She turns up at ten to nine, immaculately timed, just as he is beginning to get jumpy but comfortably before he begins to get irritated. She slips between the groups of people standing at the bar and comes over to him

She is wearing a very plain, charcoal-grey cashmere dress, a black suede jacket, and black suede pumps with modest heels. Bare brown legs, despite the chill November night. Her hair done up loosely on top with a little silk scarf. He has observed at least two men watching her as she crosses the bar.

"What'll you have?"

"Vodka with ice," she says. "Oh, make it a double. What the hell, it's Friday night."

My pleasure, he thinks evilly. He buys her drink and rejoins her on the sofa. She sits cross-legged and half-turned towards him. This is the best bit, he thinks suddenly. Nothing else beats this moment. Nothing.

As the evening wears on she becomes more and more animated. Something in her expression seems to him pointed and meaningful, and loaded with significance.

"Let's talk about you," he says. "I still don't feel I really know anything about you. I mean, where did you grow up? Where did you go to school?"

"Hampshire."

"And what sort of school?"

She thinks for a short while and then says, "A Reformatory."

"Really?"

"Oh yes. She lays one hand on his knee. I was a very naughty girl."

"How naughty?" he asks provocatively.

"Very naughty," she says. "I was at a Reformatory run by nuns, for the Very Naughtiest Girls in England. And they were the Little Sisters of Discipline and Stern Reproof."

"Stern…?" he says, going goggle-eyed.

"Reproof" she repeats, patting him on the knee again. "And Discipline. Very strict they were too. Any little breach of the rules and you were severely punished. You were only allowed to walk, not run, down the Marble Corridor, for instance, on the way to 4am Matins, no matter how late you were."

"And you were caught running?"

"Oh no, I was caught flying. Well, not really flying, but certainly floating down the corridor, a couple of feet off the floor. But Sister Felicita was furious. She said she had never encountered anything so impertinent since her days as a foreman on a building site. And I had to be severely punished."

"Go on," he says.

"Well, I was taken to the Mother Superior's study, and there the Mother Superior and Sister Felicita and Sister Perpetua made me bend down across the leather-topped desk."

"Yes?"

She sighs coyly. "And…well, they made me hitch up my little gymslip."

"You wore gymslips? That doesn't seem a very good idea for a Reformatory for Very Naughty Girls."

"Little gymslips," she stresses. "Very short

they were." She plucks up the hem of her dress until it covers only the very upper reaches of her thighs, and she looks at him wide-eyed. "That short at least," she says. She pulls it down again demurely. "Oh, it was to put temptation in our way," she explains. "We were always being told that the world was such a terribly wicked place, and before we were released back into society, we had to learn to be able to resist temptation. That was also the reason why all girls had to share double or even triple beds in communal dormitories, right up to the sixth form. And why the school uniform was always so deliberately...well, so skimpy, and sexy: gymslips, black stockings, high-heeled shoes, blouses that had to have at least the top four buttons undone at all times. And at bedtime, these really short, lacy nighties. And all the walls of our dormitories were decorated with these enormous, and most inflammatory, murals depicting acts of...well..."

"Well?"

She lowers her eyes to her feet and plays little-girlishly with the hem of her dress. "Well," she whispers. "Sapphic love."

He swallows. When he speaks his voice is hoarse.

"Go on," he says, with a certain, undignified desperation.

"And all the bedside cupboards had...well, you know...things in them."

"Things?"

"Things," she repeats solemnly. "Anyway, the day I was caught floating down the Marble Corridor, I was made to bend over this leather-topped desk, and hitch my little gymslip up around my waist. And then...actually, I wouldn't mind another drink, would you?"

He looks around with wild impatience, unseeing, and says OK then, and takes the proffered note from her and buys a couple more drinks and returns in remarkably quick time. She is sitting back looking very relaxed and smoking a cigarette. She has been musing on how ridiculously easy it is to turn men on, how predictable their tastes in erotic tales. And yet how she loves doing it. And this particular man, she admits, is very sweet: the rueful, apologetic smile, the awkward hand movements, the inarticulate mumblings.

"Well?" he says.

"Oh, thank you darling," she says, leaning forwards for her glass and taking a sip.

"No, I mean...well?"

"Well what?"

"The spanking, the spanking!" he hisses.

She looks at him blankly for a moment and then laughs and touches him on the arm. "Oh I'm sorry, I'd quite forgotten. Now where was I?"

"Over the leather-topped desk," he says. "Your gymslip up around your waist."

"Quite so," she says, drawing deeply on her

cigarette. "You have been paying attention, haven't you?"

"I'm...I'm interested. From a purely, urm...erotic-philosophical point of view."

She eyes him with amusement as he sits there, on the edge of his seat, twitching at every cruel flick of her narrative whip. "Well," she resumes. "There I was, with my very short, tight gymslip hitched right up. And Sister Felicita started to spank me on the bottom with her bare hand. But after a while she stopped and said to the Mother Superior, 'I'm afraid that young Miss Elizabeth is a particularly recalcitrant young lady. I suggest that she requires chastisement on her bare flesh.' The Mother Superior gave her assent, and so Sister Felicita and Sister Perpetua promptly positioned themselves either side of me and ordered me to part my legs a little. Then I felt two pairs of hands pulling my knickers down to my ankles. Then they both started spanking me again at the same time, on my bare buttocks."

"Then...then what?"

"That's...that's it. They told me to put my clotehs back on and be off to lessons."

"Oh," he says disappointed.

"You sound disappointed."

"No, not at all. I just...I just thought it might get more..."

"Men!" she tuts. "You're all the same. You only ever think of one thing."

"No, that's not true!" he protests. "I love fantasies and the build-up and all that bit. But in the end...well, you want the Happy Ending, don't you? You don't want to be left in the lurch."

"Hm," she says, circling her fingertip round the rim of her glass (already empty again) and looking steadily at him. "I don't know. I like the fantasy bit just as much. And you don't have to feel so guilty. After all, it's not actually doing it, is it?"

"No. No. It's not actually doing it," he agrees. "So...so you mean, just, like fantasizing with each other is OK, as long as it doesn't go any further?"

"I can't see anything wrong with it, can you?"

"No, nothing at all."

They have two more drinks before closing time and then rise to leave.

"I'll get a cab in Fulham Road," she says.

"Oh, I'll walk you," he says. "Save you the cab fare."

"And anyway," he adds, "when I get you home I intend to whisk you inside and up to your bedroom and fuck you senseless all night long. Though purely in fantasy, of course. I can't see anything wrong with that, can you?"

"How very rude," she says, and then smiles. "Come on, then."

This short story first appeared in The Erotic Review *(see page 319).*

"S", with its curvaceous, wriggling form, is a rampant kind of letter, romping through some of the more salacious aspects of sexual practice, from the relatively tame soixante-neuf to the sadistic shenanigans of the Marquis de Sade and modern-day SM.

Soixante-neuf This used to be the considered the *crème de la crème* of oral gratification but it seems now to have lost some of its cachet. It's fine for those who can concentrate on two things at once – those famed multi-taskers amongst us – but for others, focusing on pleasing their partner at the same time as pleasing themselves is too much like hard work. And sex shouldn't be hard work. But if you lighten up and take a broad-brush approach to it, noshing each other's genitals with relish rather than trying to deliver the perfect blow- or face-job, then the drug-like effect of lust will kick in and you will be transported to sex heaven.

Sade, Marquis de

The infamous Marquis de Sade (1740–1814), after whom the pioneering sexologist Krafft-Ebing coined the term "sadism" some 120 years later, has undergone something of a reconstruction in recent times. Poor old love, it wasn't his fault that he was so debauched and cruel, what with being spoilt by his female relatives when he was young and corrupted by his uncle. Add to that the context of a country revelling in a state of unparalleled libertinage, with bad King Louis XV running amok in his Deer Park with his innumerable mistresses, and the streets chock-full of bordellos and prostitutes. Make no mistake, this is a man you definitely wouldn't want to have met on a dark night, nor in daylight, for that matter, as Rose Keller had the misfortune of doing. The story goes that against her will she was stripped naked, tied to a bed, repeatedly beaten, and cuts made in her flesh, into which de Sade poured large amounts of sealing wax. He also threatened to kill her if she didn't stop screaming. But he didn't have sex with her. Small wonder that his mother-in-law contrived to have him locked up.

SM

This stands for sadomasochism, and we now know, thanks to de Sade, all about the "sado", or gaining sexual gratification from inflicting pain on others, part. The same Krafft-Ebing also came up with the term for the counterbalance – "Masochism", named after Leopold von Sacher-Masoch, he of the fur fetish and a fondness for being flagellated – or sexual satisfaction from receiving pain (specifically at the hands of a woman in Sacher-Masoch's case). Like BD, or bondage/submission and domination (but not to be confused with), SM is a controlled sex game played between two consenting adults in a balanced partnership. In a heterosexual pairing, it is often the woman who metes out the "punishment" but by no means exclusively. Every individual's pain threshold is different, so this needs to be explored and levels agreed. Having said that, during the action, the brain releases endorphins that have a euphoric effect and dull pain, but this rapidly ceases after orgasm, so the "discipline" must stop then.

Stripping Gypsy Rose Lee is the most famous female stripper of all time. The seductive dance moves and theatrical teasing characteristic of her act succeeded in turning stripping into something of an art form in the 1930s, thereby earning it an unlikely respectability. Blaze Starr was another renowned classic stripper who came to the fore in the '50s and whose trademark performance featured a rousing rendition on the jungle drums as an accompaniment to an appropriately exotic dance routine. For her considerable talents she was dubbed "the hottest blaze in burlesque". In more recent times, an entirely new chapter on stripping was opened, when The Chippendales took the world by storm. Britain made its own unique, typically understated, introspective, and comic contribution to the genre with the film *The Full Monty*, in which a group of unemployed steelworkers bare both body and soul.

Swinging This used to be known as "wife-swapping" back in the '60s and '70s when sexual liberation was in full swing. This was when, in outwardly respectable provincial communities, people gathered together for a party, after getting suitable legless, dropped their house keys into the empty fondue, and took pot luck on an alternative partner for a night of steamy sex. Some hopes! Thankfully, things have moved on quite a way since then. Today, swinging is regarded as a "lifestyle" choice, and it's big business – certainly in the US, with Continental Europe fast catching up. A vast network of swing clubs and activities has been established, and or course the Internet has served to spread the swinging word. A popular option is to take a swinging vacation, where a couple can stay in a specially orchestrated environment, often with nude sunbathing and bathing facilities plus other hedonistic options on tap – not tacky but all very tasteful. Perhaps surprisingly to the uninitiated, the scene appeals to those in a stable, long-term relationship who are emotionally confident enough to enjoy sexual extensions and explorations without fear of wrecking their relationships. In other words, this is recreational sex.

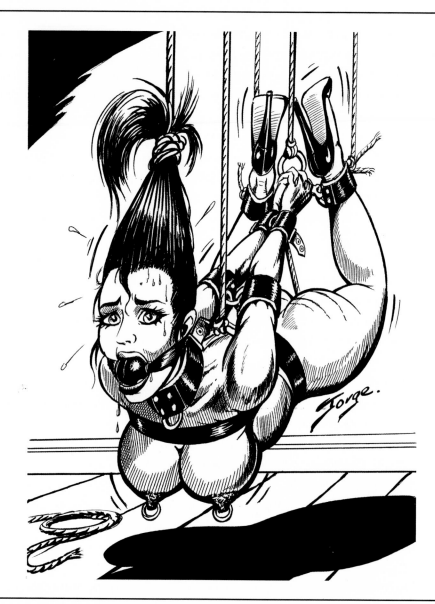

Terry Wakelin (www.olympia-press.co.uk)

The Seasons of Sex

*Now the freezin' cold does shrink my cock
And I have heard a woollen sock
Will do man a better deed
Than wicked spillin' of his seed.*

***

*Hooray! Hooray! The first of May
Outdoor fucking begins today!*

***

*When the weather's hot and sticky,
Then it's time for dunkin' dickie*

***

*When the frost is on the pumkin'
T'is the time for dickie dunkin'*

***

*When the gorse no longer is in flower
Kissing is out of season*

Traditional songs/sayings

Peter Fendi (1796–1842)

S is for Seductive Sex

Come With Me

Stephen Bayley

Gregory the Great demanded that a seducer of a virgin, whatever that is, must marry her or, failing the discharge of this honourable obligation, suffer severe corporal punishment before being banged up in a monastery to perform enduring and solitary penance.

St Thomas Aquinas said that lust, even in the slightest degree, was a mortal sin. The liberals among the doctors of the church allowed that a premarital touch of the hand was acceptable provided only that absolutely no sexual feelings were stimulated.

So, nuzzling the ear, inhaling shampoo, quickening breath, muttering poetry, solidifying and liquefying groins, a firm breast in one hand, knicker elastic in the other, a shuffling of position, an arching back, a click, a snap, a bustle, a zip, a "don't" and then a "do", an "ooh" and an "ah". This is modern life.

Somewhere between the Middle Ages and now we developed sophisticated stratagems of seduction. Ovid's *Ars Amatoria* was an important Roman predecessor of the how-to book, a welcome rediscovery of the Renaissance. The art of courtly love – or how to get your leg over an obstinate strumpet with the help of troubadours – was defined in a 12th-century treatise by Andreas Capellanus. Castiglione, Machiavelli, Gracian, and later Choderlos de la Clos, not to mention Casanova, all contributed to the body of expertise in getting a reluctant woman to make the journey from no to yes. All these great philosophers of manners have their champions, although some say Terry Southerri's *Flash and Filigree* (1958) is the masterpiece of the genre. Here the man calms his voice while arousing with his hands,

although the inept get it the wrong way around. "No. Not there, you idiot" for some reason comes echoing back into the cavernous hall of memory.

So. Seduction. How do you do it? I think tact is important. In normal circumstances I don't find the gallant invitation "Do you want to fuck me, big boy?" much of an inducement, although it is quite unusual, thus achieving the interesting condition of being both rare and worthless. John Gay's *The Beggar's Opera* says:

'Tis woman that seduces all mankind. By her we first were taught the wheedling arts.

I'm not sure wheedling does much for me either. Equally, I think most men don't like women's initiative in this area. I used to know a successful couple in property development who visited building sites in a burgundy Rolls-Royce Camargue with cream upholstery. The wife was a handsome woman with lustrous hair down to her waist and an astonishing dress-sense which included fishnet tights, leather hotpants, stiletto patent boots, a leopard-skin handbag, and translucent black shirt with a great deal going on underneath. I asked her why and she said it was a navvy-survival technique. Brute men on sites were so taken aback they were muted.

Again, a 1980s entrepreneur claimed that the scariest moment he had had was when, at tea in Downing Street, the Prime Minister put her hand on his leg, looked him in the eye, and said, "You know something? It is very lonely for a woman here."

I have my own contender. Years ago at a conference I sat next to exactly the sort of woman I find stirringly attractive. French. Simple skirt, good shoes, plain cashmere V-neck. Nice hair, the accent, a twinkle in the eye, bookish, but dangerous with an untipped Gitane. We progressed to dinner and I was loving it all until, back in the car, she said, "And now I want you to drive me to the country, remove my *petite culottes*, and have me in a field."

This was Bloomsbury in central London at midnight, so you can see the problem. Or take Norman Lewis, as another French woman tried to at a dreadful Embassy dinner. Next to him at table she lifted her skirt and said *"Voulez-vous voir ma petite craque?"* This doesn't work. Instead, a flick of the hair, an indeterminate sigh, and a distracted look are what does it for me. Although if by any chance Natalie is reading this, I hope you agree I made up for it by the time we got to Amersham.

Like Natalie, my own stratagems are now history; now that the relative certainties of marriage have replaced the vagaries of independent life. But, thinking back, it was John Gay who, again, understood seducers' techniques:

What cannot a neat knave with a smooth tale make a woman believe?

When I was a neat knave I always found Andrew Marvel's "To His Coy Mistress" worked wonders. It was written as a seducer's manifesto, but you had to be certain that the listener was sensitive to nuance. More direct approaches can work too. We have all known someone who has said the practice of asking every woman he met whether she would like to "tear her pleasure with rough strife through the iron gates of life" right now yields surprisingly high statistical positives. I have never, alas, tried this, although I recall there was one striking success when, despairing of subtleties, I simply had the nerve to say, "I've come here ['here' was West Hampstead, so it was no laughing matter] tonight because I think you're the most attractive woman I have ever met." Minutes later, the fragrances of an unfamiliar bedroom. That was a lie and it felt like it the next morning.

The seducer, especially the male seducer, is always on dubious moral ground because the concept implies an element of coercion. The erotic element in seduction is not just the hoped-for climax at the top of the sexual mountain, but the element of power relations involved in all the processes required on the lower slopes. Rather as Stirling Moss once said of motor racing that, "If it wasn't dangerous, anyone could do it", with seduction, it's the same. While the joyful spasm of the groin might be a welcome brute pleasure, if every one was just there to be had on demand, then an orgasm would not be so very much different to a sneeze (which it happens to resemble neurologically). If seduction was not so difficult, it would not be so engrossing.

And it can still be dangerous. One of my favourite novellas is Nathanial West's *Miss Lonelyhearts* (1933). Here the narrator, a male agony columnist, seduces a frustrated reader out of charity and, as I recall, gets shot for his kindness. As ever it's best (not?) to think about it.

This article first appeared in The Erotic Review *(see page 319).*

The letter "T" heads off in multiple directions and so is an exploratory character. It takes us on a titillating journey, guiding us through the bewildering realm of sex Toys to the mystical movements of Tantric sex, down Mexico way to Tijuana and safely returning to the Top shelf. Enjoy the ride!

Toys There are more sex toys, easily available by mail order or through the Internet, than you can shake a dildo at. Vibrators, vagina suckers, clitoral clips, anal beads, butt plugs, nipple clamps and chains, cock rings, in addition to the whole range of bondage accoutrements and sex-play outfits – where do you begin? You can spend many a distracting hour pouring over a catalogue, taking delivery of discreet unmarked packages and, best of all, trying out your purchases. But if you find the choice rather daunting, or you haven't got the time or the money to invest, or you just prefer being creative, use your imagination and exploit the potential in everyday items. Playing a warm jet of water over your clitoral area is subtly stimulating, while jerking off with a piece of liver is a tried-and-tested favourite. But one word of warning: don't insert anything into your anus that could disappear beyond reach, and even small objects in the vagina can prove tricky to retrieve!

Tantric Sex "Tantra" – from the Sanskrit meaning "woven together" – relates to the ancient Vedic Hindu philosophy based on the spiritual unification of masculine and feminine energies. This can be achieved with a partner or even on your own (my vote is firmly with the former). The first step towards this spiritual union, by way of sex, is through heightening the senses and elevating awareness of each other's minds and bodies. In practice, this involves synchronizing breathing and even heartbeats, moving on to harmonizing and building up energy through the chakras – the energy centres of the body – through extended foreplay (at least an hour's worth). But that's just the warm-up for the main event, which entails finding different ways of delaying orgasm for as long as possible (several hours when you know how) or even altogether, in order to reach a level of mystical consciousness and, hopefully, a state of spiritual enlightenment. Another important feature of Tantra is the divine worshipping of your partner, since he or she, according to Tantric teachings, is a manifestation of a god or goddess. We'll have to let Sting, that celebrity exponent of the art, have the last word on Tantric: "Tantric is not just about sex, it's about how you give thanks to creation for the way you walk, eat, breathe, treat other people – it's about treating your partner as a goddess."

Tattooing In yesteryear it was horse and carriage aka love and marriage. Nowadays it's piercing and tattooing aka body and modification. As we have seen with piercing, tattooing is not exactly the new alteration on the block. Indeed, Italian ice man Ötzi, aged 5,300 years, was discovered in the Alps with all of his 57 tattoos intact. And so we have tattooing through the intervening centuries for a variety of purposes, from fertility rites to tribal identification, with all the usual suspects at it, from the Ancient Egyptians to the Native Americans, with the Polynesians and the Japanese making their particular marks.

Tijuana Bibles These cheap-'n'-cheerful comic books were the under-the-counter porno of late '20s to early '50s America. Some 700–1,000 of these Eight-Pager booklets were anonymously drawn, clandestinely produced, and hungrily devoured by a rank-and-file readership throughout the lean years of the Depression, desperate for a little light relief – and sex education, for that matter. They took as their focus the imagined sexual exploits of the Hollywood heroes, cartoon characters, and other cult figures of the day, including Ingrid Bergman, Cary Grant, and James Cagney; Mae West, Greta Garbo, and Clara Bow; along with Hitler, Mussolini, and Stalin – not forgetting Gandhi. Among these prurient parodies appears one memorable depiction of Donald Duck of Disney fame mounting Minnie Mouse. The attitudes and artistic skills showcased in these publications may not stand up to contemporary close scrutiny, but their directness and reckless irreverence have a welcome ring of innocence and honesty. As Art Spiegelman sums up in his introduction to the book *Tijuana Bibles: Art and Wit in America's Forbidden Funnies, 1930s–1950s*, "They portray a buoyant, priapic world in which lust overcomes everything, even bad drawing, bad grammar, bad jokes, and bad printing."

Touch When you consider that the skin is the body's largest organ, it's hardly surprising that the power of plain and simple touching is so great. Any area of the skin's surface can become sexually sensitized to touch, and when the body is in a state of full-blown arousal, all kinds of unexpected areas can become sexually charged. The potential excitement to be derived from fondling the so-called erogenous zones is not to be underestimated, and not everyone's pleasure points are the same. Women's nipples are a safe bet, you would have thought, but one of the pair can be much more responsive than the other. Feet have a mass of nerve endings, but an unskilled assault could end in wails of laughter rather than ecstasy. However, for some, sucking the toes is an exquisite experience.

Eric Wilkins (Contemporary)

Sergeant *Tally-Ho*

Oh, I am a rough and rambling youth, in America now I do reside,
And for the courtin' of these pretty girls, I've travelled this country far and wide;
I've been all over America, I've travelled in England, France, and Spain,
And I have been in Germany and now, by gosh, I'm going home.

Refrain:

Li ti li ful lol a fa lur a leer a laddy O
Li ti ful lal whack fal al eer.

Now the colonel's wife she's heard of me and heard I was a willing youth,
And begged of me most earnestly if she could see the naked truth;
So I pulled out my lusty pin, as much as her two hands could span.
Right to the bedroom she led me saying, "You shall be my handy man."

Refrain.

Northern Californian folk song from the 1930s

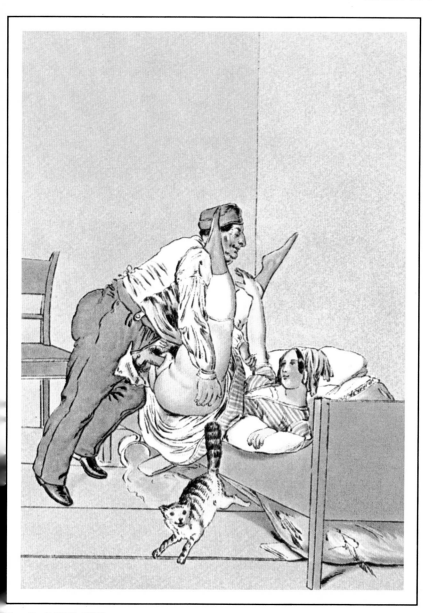

Peter Fendi (1796–1842)

T is for Therese Philosophe

Therese Philosophe

The Marquis d'Argens

The venerable Father Dirrag opened his fly. A throbbing arrow shot out of his trousers which looked exactly like that fateful snake which my former father confessor had warned me about so vehemently.

The monster was as long and as thick and as heavy as the one about which the Capuchine monk had made all those dire predictions. I shivered with delightful horror. The red head of this snake seemed to threaten Eradice's behind which had taken on a deep pink coloration because of the slaps it had received during the Bible recitation. The face of Father Dirrag perspired and was flushed a deep red.

"And now," he said, "you must separate your soul from the senses. And if my dear daughter has not disappointed my pious hopes, she shall neither feel, nor hear, nor see anything."

Then with his bare hand he released a torrent of slaps on Eradice's naked buttocks. However, she did not say a word. I noticed only an occasional twitching of her bum, a sort of spasming and relaxing at the rhythm of the priest's blows.

"I am very satisfied with you," he told her after he had punished her for about five minutes in this manner. "The time has come when you are going to reap the fruits of your holy labours. Don't question me, my dear daughter, but be guided by God's will, which is working through me. Throw yourself, face down, upon the floor; I will now expel the last traces of impurity with a sacred relic. It is part of the venerable rope which girded the waist of the holy Saint Francis himself."

The good priest put Eradice in a position which was extremely fitting for what he had in mind. I had never seen my girlfriend in such a beautiful position. Her buttocks were half-opened and the double path to satisfaction was wide-open.

After the old lecher had admired her for a while, he moistened his so-called rope of Saint Francis with spittle, murmured some of the priestly mumbo-jumbo which these gentlemen generally use to exorcise the devil, and proceeded to shove the rope into my friend.

I could watch the entire operation from my little hideout. The windows of the room were opposite the door of the alcove behind which Eradice had hidden me. She was kneeling on the floor, her arms were crossed over the footstool, and her head rested upon her folded arms. Her skirts, which had been carefully folded up to her shoulders, revealed her marvellous buttocks and the beautiful curve of her back. This exciting view did not escape the attention of the venerable Father Dirrag. His gaze feasted upon the view for quite some time. He had clamped the legs of his penitent between his own legs, and his hands held the monstrous rope.

He lingered for some time in this devotional position and inspected the altar with glowing eyes. He seemed to be undecided how to effect his sacrifice, since there were two inviting openings. His eyes devoured both and it seemed as if he were unable to make up his mind. The top one was a well-known delight for a priest, but, after all, he had also promised a taste of Heaven to his penitent. What was he to do? Several times he knocked with the tip of his tool at the gate he desired most, but finally, I must do him justice, I saw his monstrous prick disappear the natural way, after his priestly fingers had carefully parted the rosy lips of Eradice's lovepit.

The labour started with about three forceful shoves which made him enter about halfway. And suddenly the seeming calmness of the priest changed into some sort of fury. My God, what a change! Mouth half-open, lips foam-flecked, teeth gnashing and snorting like a bull about to attack a cud-chewing cow. However, he measured his shoving very carefully, seeing to it that he never left her lovepit and also that his belly never touched her arse. He did not want his penitent to find out to whom the holy relic of Saint Francis was connected! What an incredible presence of mind!

I could see that about an inch of the holy tool constantly remained on the outside and never took part in the festivities. I could see that with every backward movement of the priest the red lips of Eradice's love-nest opened and I remember clearly that the vivid pink colour was a most charming sight. However, whenever the good priest shoved forward, the lips closed and I could see only the finely curled hairs which covered them. They clamped around the priestly tool so firmly that it seemed as if they had devoured the holy arrow. It looked for all the world like both of them were connected to Saint Francis' relic and it was hard to guess which one of the two persons was the true possessor of this holy tool.

What a sight, especially for a young girl who knew nothing about these secrets. The most amazing thoughts ran through my head, but they all were rather vague and I could not find proper words for them. I only remember that I wanted to throw myself at the feet of this famous father confessor and beg him to exorcise me the same way he was blessing my dear friend. Was this piety? Or carnal desire? Even today I could not tell you for sure.

But let us go back to our devout couple! The movements of the priest quickened; he was barely able to keep his balance. His body formed an "S" from head to toe whose frontal bulge moved rapidly back and forth in a horizontal line.

"Is your spirit receiving any satisfaction, my dear little saint?" he asked with a deep sigh. "I, myself, can see Heaven open up. God's infinite mercy is about to remove me from this vale of tears, I ..."

"Oh, venerable Father," exclaimed Eradice, "I cannot describe the delights that are flowing through me! Oh, yes, yes, I experience Heavenly bliss. I can feel how my spirit is being liberated from all earthly desires. Please, please, dearest Father, exorcise every last impurity remaining upon my tainted soul. I can see...the angels of God...push stronger... ooh...shove the holy relic deeper...deeper. Please, dearest Father, shove it as hard as you can... Ooooh!...oooh!!! Dearest holy Saint Francis...Ooh, good saint...please, don't leave me in the hour of my greatest need... I feel your relic...it is so good...your...holy...relic... I can't hold it any longer...I am...dying!"

The priest also felt his climax approach. He shoved, slammed, snorted, and groaned. And then he stopped and pulled out. I saw the proud snake. It had become very meek and small. It crawled out of its hole, foam-covered, with hanging head.

What else shall I tell you? Dirrag left, Eradice opened the door to the alcove, and embraced me, crying out, "Oh, my dearest Therese. Partake of my joy and delight. Yes, yes, today I have seen paradise. I have shared the delights of the angels. The incredible joy, my dearest friend, the incomparable price for but one moment of pain! Thanks to the holy rope of Saint Francis my soul almost left its earthly vessel. You have seen how my good father confessor introduced the relic into me. I swear that I could feel it touch my heart. Just a little deeper and I would have joined the saints in paradise!"

"U" descends not quite to the depths but to the baseline, and proceeding in reverse it brings us the art of divestment, Undressing. Before removing it, we have the opportunity to analyse the allure of Underwear — a fishnet pouch for him, say, and a boned basque for her. From its lowly position, our character achieves the Under and over form of coupling.

Under and Over

This is a surprisingly different mode of lovemaking, sensual and languorous – perfect for long, sultry afternoons. It's rear entry but not as we generally know it or think of it. With the genital contact being offset, the rest of her and his body are curiously liberated, even though they appear entirely entangled. There is much opportunity for passionate kissing and caressing along the way. By keeping her knees together, she tightens her vaginal grip but also applies a gentle pressure to the clitoral area.

Underpants The clothing and adornment of the nether regions has had a chequered history. It was men's fashion in this regard that took the initial lead, with the cult of the codpiece. This had been a feature of men's attire in the Middle Ages basically as a means of preserving male modesty by covering the gap in the two halves of the hose, which the doublet, being so wickedly short, would otherwise reveal. However, the heyday of the codpiece as a fashion accessory came later, particularly during the reign of King Henry VIII of England, when it became padded, ornamented, and of outrageous proportions. Women's apparel of the privates in the Western world was, on the other hand, a largely utilitarian affair, undergarments being worn down the ages to keep bodily grime from straying, exclude the cold, and protect the delicate parts from scratchy outer garments. Apart from a brief flirtation with underpants in Renaissance Venice, this particular form of underwear was rejected as being essentially masculine. Ironically, the first "modern" knickers for adults were deemed decidedly naughty, being worn only by flaunting prostitutes and dancers. But the idea soon caught on and by the latter part of the 19th century lingerie was not only a fashion item in its own right but an acknowledged seductive force.

Undressing Whether it's taking off our own clothes or someone else's, the sensual pleasures of undressing are not to be thrown aside in an unseemly haste to get one's kecks off. One can never, however, hope to recapture the wonder of those early tactile expeditions of youth, and the electric sensation of discovery when a new layer of clothing had been breached. Even in those circumstances, a certain artistry of approach was required, particularly on the part of the lads – the swift, unfumbled, single-handed unhooking of the bra was a practised skill. The trick is to play out that final revelation to the tantalizing last, lingering on each layer and always keeping a little concealment in reserve.

Unprotected Sex Riding bareback, or having sex without using a condom, is a health risk – it's as simple as that. If you have been in a monogamous relationship for some considerable time, then the risk of STIs – sexually transmitted infections, which include HIV – is probably minimal. But anything short of that and the risk factor increases, since no one can be certain about the sexual history of all the interrelationships that are involved even in the most modest of sexual profiles. And some sexual practices – anal in particular – carry a greater risk than others. Barrier protection, in all its present-day array of dazzling colours, tempting flavours, and teasing textures, has come an awful long way from what were termed "overcoats", the crude precursors of condoms that, hardly a study in sensitivity, were so heavy-duty they could be rinsed out and used again.

Urtication Some will know this practice as a traditional remedy for rheumatic and arthritic pain; others may recognize it as a traditional treatment for paralysis. The term denotes the process of using stinging nettles to stimulate the skin. But we've not moved into the realms of herbal medicine here – we're still talking about sex, baby. When I add that stinging nettles were often applied to the affected parts in a flogging or swatting motion, you will doubtless begin to get the sexual angle. It's actually one of the simplest, safest SM techniques, as long as there is no allergic reaction. After the initial sharp stinging sensation, there follows a long aftermath of several hours in which a pleasant warm tingling is experienced in the target area. It also has the effect of sensitizing the skin so that a mere flick of a feather may well produce an expression of ecstasy. Urtication was a speciality of some of the most notable female flagellants of old London town in the 19th century, including one Mrs Collett, on whose list of illustrious clients was none other than George IV. She was reported as keeping vases filled with a constant supply of green nettles, along with many other more conventional instruments of sexual torture.

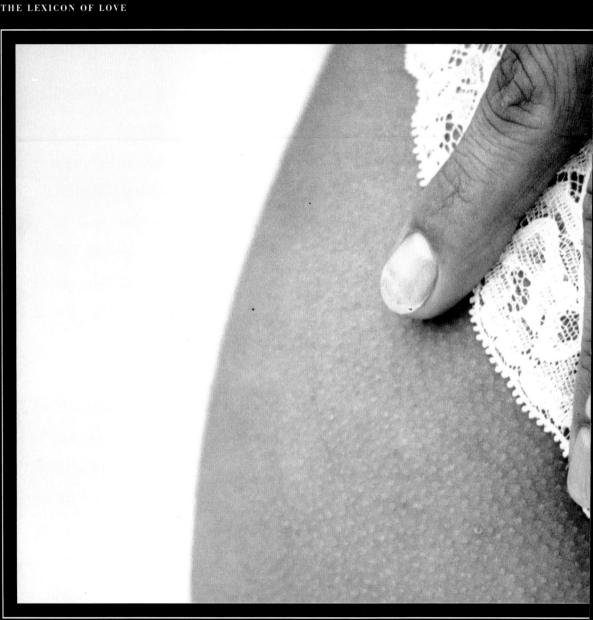

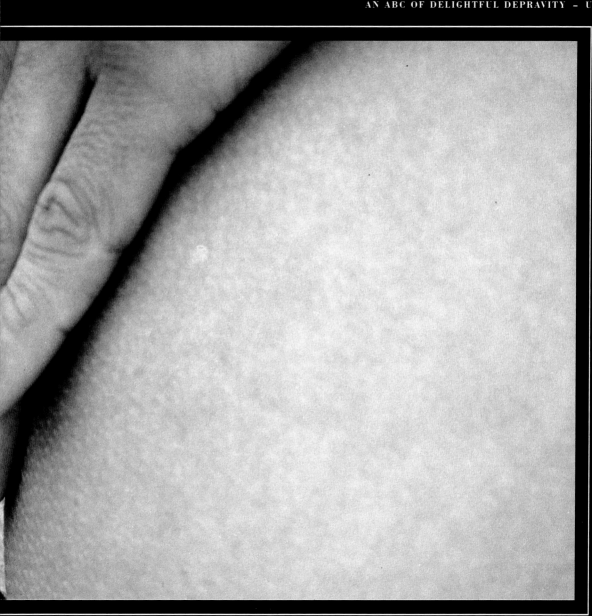

Uncontrollable passions...

Good God, what a night that was,
The bed was so soft, and how we clung,
Burning together, lying this way and that,
*Our **uncontrollable passions***
Flowing through our mouths.
If I could only die that way,
I'd say goodbye to the business of living.

Petronius (1st century AD), translated from the Greek by Kenneth Rexroth

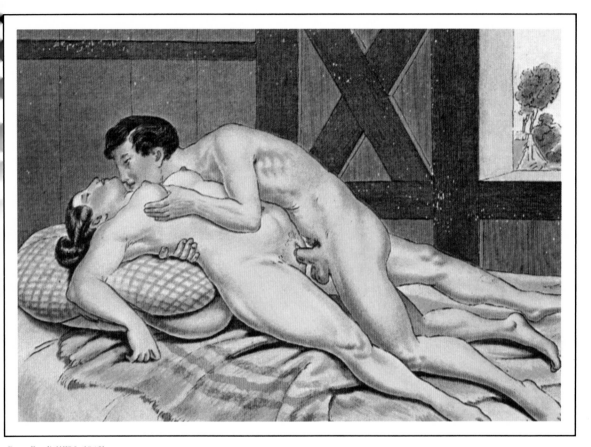

Peter Fendi (1796–1842)

U is for Unbridled

Unbridled

Forum magazine

Henderson paused. The house said money. Its open front door said nice neighbourhood. The hesitant way Henderson knocked said he wished he'd hired something with tails. But it wasn't really business. Just a friend asking him to drop by, do a friend of a friend a favour.

"We're upstairs. Shut the door behind you!" The bride stood at the end of the room, twirling, admiring herself. A petticoat-swelled dress leaped from a narrow waist to skim the bedroom carpet, its tight bodice revealing tighter stomach, symmetrical ribcage, and cupped breasts.

Henderson froze in the doorway, studying the shadowy curve of her cleavage, the line of her collarbone, the bare shoulders, swan neck, elegant arms swathed in taut gloves, hands playing fussily in her blonde hair.

"You're Henderson? Marguerita's friend?"

She continued admiring herself in the mirror, hardly concerning herself with him.

"Margie showed me your pictures. I really liked them," she continued, disdaining introduction. But she turned to give him her full attention, sizing him up, having first checked him out in the mirror.

Henderson envied the dress. He envied the groom – wondered if he could handle her.

"Sorry," Henderson said, "I don't do weddings." His brain told him he wanted to do this one! "I take portraits of people. At work and play."

"Especially play," she added. "Was Margie work or play?"

He realized which pictures Margie had shown her. He caught a glimpse of himself in several mirrors, blushing furiously.

Maybe she guessed why Margie looked so aroused and wanton in the photos. Maybe Margie had told her, explained that he'd tried to take her portrait while deep inside her, had wanted a picture of her as she came, capturing the orgasm…but couldn't focus, couldn't hold the camera steady enough.

The bride swept across the bedroom, skirts sighing on the carpet. Henderson wondered if she was wearing stockings and a garter. He imagined her thighs.

"I'd like some pictures for my husband-to-be." She paused, pensive. "Something special. Something the wedding photographs won't give us."

The noise made him look away. The mirrored en suite bathroom door had opened. For a moment he panicked, praying it wasn't the "husband-to-be".

The woman who entered was in her mid-twenties, like the bride, but was clad in tight blue jeans and loose-fitting denim shirt.

She looked familiar, and then he placed her. She was a friend of Margie's! He'd met her once. Briefly. She gave no sign of recognizing him; she simply smiled, then looked at the bride. They giggled.

"He'll do," said the bridesmaid.

She stepped behind the bride. Moments later, the dress was divorced from its wearer, to be carefully transported across the room and hung away in a mirrored closet.

Henderson's eyes bulged. He tried not to

stare at her, but wherever he looked in the room he could see a panorama of the defrocked bride mirrored on every wall.

She wore a white, strapless bra, cupping and uplifting her breasts, displaying them, barely hiding them. A thin lacy white ribbon of panty arched up between her legs and curved round bronze thighs. She retained the long, elegant white gloves, balancing the long, elegant white stockings. And she kept on the one splash of colour. A blue garter.

"Will this do?" she asked, hands sliding across her body. "I want my fiancé to have something special." She eased on to the bed and knelt there, a provocative kitten.

"I'm keen on photography myself. I've had Margie pose for me, too."

Henderson felt something pressing against the inside of his pants, imagining the bride, with Margie posing. He wondered if the bride had kept the camera focused.

"What exactly did you want?" His voice sounded hoarse.

"I want a portrait of me as I come. I want you to capture the expression on my face, the gleam in my eyes. I want pictures he can hear."

He wanted to see her come. He wanted to be there to photograph it.

"I know it won't be easy," she said, a mischievous grin written across her face.

Henderson watched as she slowly peeled the glove from her right arm, finally flourishing it with the vaudeville panache of a stripper. Her naked fingers moved to the inside of her thighs and began systematically tickling the smooth flesh.

"I get a bit wild when I come. Forgive me if I forget to smile for the camera."

"Is your friend just here to watch, or can I use her?"

They both giggled.

"She's here as my chaperone. I wouldn't want my husband thinking I'd been alone with some strange man, would I? Not looking the way I'll look in the picture."

They both laughed.

Henderson had a small, portable reflector in his holdall. He handed it to the bridesmaid. "Hold this for me, will you?"

She took it and allowed him to manoeuvre her into position on the bed's edge. The reflected light complemented the bride's tan and added highlights to her blonde hair.

"Ready when you are," he confirmed, framing her face in the viewfinder. He was in control, now, the consummate professional. She was just a model. Just another model. And his prick was throbbing, wishing those naked fingers were playing with it.

She leaned back slightly. Her eyes began to drift away, somewhere secret. Her fingers described little circles in the tufts of downy gold hair that peeked from under her panties. She began to rock slightly, the muscles in her thighs tensing and relaxing, tensing and relaxing.

She was in no hurry. She enjoyed the attention. Slow, self-absorbed, enjoying each moment.

Her breathing became deeper until it was the only sound he could hear. Until Henderson realized the bridesmaid was breathing deeply as well.

The bride tugged at her panties with her free hand, pulling the flimsy fabric into her, a tight little ribbon of white silk lost in blonde hairs and pink flesh. Henderson watched the silk turn into a slender, damp cord, sinking deeper into the swelling.

The gold light danced wildly in her hair. He glanced at the bridesmaid. She held the reflector in one hand, rubbing the front of her jeans with the other. He caught her glancing at the bulge in his pants, her mouth open.

Henderson moved closer to her, as if changing his camera angle. He allowed his leg to brush against her thigh, as if by accident. She didn't pull away; if anything, she pressed against him. He adjusted, brushing against her again, thigh against thigh, until he had manoeuvred behind, getting a better angle for the shot, his knee slipping up on to the bed, resting against her bum.

Henderson reached down, touched her hand, adjusting the mirror, letting his fingers track their way up her arm, leaning his

camera on her shoulder, allowing his weight to press on her. She leaned back against him, flicking her head, encouraging his fingers to stroke her hand.

"Yes!" The bride was looking at Henderson, nodding to her friend. "Yes!"

The reflector wobbled as the bridesmaid began rubbing herself against him. He caught a handful of her hair, tugging it rhythmically. She gripped his bum with her free hand, then followed the north circular round to discover his bulge and thrill to its hardness.

He held the camera steady, concentrating on the bride, watching her distant eyes savouring the bridesmaid's attentions.

She'd abandoned the reflector, now. Had turned, devoting all her fingers to his belt, his jeans, his zip…searching inside.

And all the time he kept watching the bride through the viewfinder, tongue moistening her lips, fingers moist in those other lips, her breath coming faster and faster.

The bridesmaid had Henderson in her hand now, grooming him firmly. He had to concentrate on focusing. "Undo your shirt," he whispered. "Take them out for me."

The bride nodded encouragement, her face radiantly drunk…

"*V*" *is a strong, bold, upstanding letter — the very epitomy of Virility. Yet impaling the baseline as it does, there is the suggestion of a little pain involved (albeit erotically pleasurable), as we shall discover in Le Vice Anglais and the vagaries of the Victorians.*

Vibrator

"Vibes" have come a long way from the absurdly buzzing, cold and brutal faux phalluses of yesteryear. They now come in a whole variety of different materials, textures, and colours, not to mention constructions. The most useful are the combo kind, which stimulate the vagina simultaneously with the clitoris, plus optional anal tickler. They also offer a variation of rhythms as well as speeds so that you can enjoy throbbing and pulsating in addition to vibration. And most are much quieter than their prototypes. In short, the vibrator has finally come of age, giving satisfaction rather than disappointment and embarrassment.

Vice Anglais, Le

The French, in their coining of this expression in the 18th century, which has stuck ever since, were quick to recognize that flagellation had found its natural home on English soil, although it whipped up something of a cult following throughout Europe at that time. One can only suppose that it was the long-established tradition of caning in schools that predisposed the English to a seemingly insatiable appetite for corporal punishment in adult life. Others have speculated that it was something to do with the inclement weather…

Victorian Sex

The Victorians were, in fact, obsessed with sex, galvanized into an attack on its every manifestation in the fear that it would threaten the newly constructed family values of the upwardly mobile bourgeoisie. In practice, the art of sexual repression, for which they are especially noted, meant spending a good deal of energy studying and defining sexual behaviour and practices before setting about crusading against them, outlawing them, or "curing" them in the name of modern medical and other burgeoning sciences. Masturbation was declared a "solitary vice", with parents engaged in a constant vigil to detect any signs of childhood sexuality in order to nip it in the bud. The latter was less a figure of expression than a reality, with boys' penises being burned, treated with electric shocks, sewn up, or encased in anti-masturbation contraptions. In a society in which people covered up furniture legs for modesty's sake, prostitution was rife – in London alone prostitute numbers were estimated at 80,000 out of a population of two million plus in the latter part of the 19th century. Underground erotica proliferated, including three astonishingly pornographic magazines: *The Cremorne, The Boudoir*, and *The Pearl*.

Virile Member This delightful term for the penis comes courtesy of the ancient Arabic guide to lovemaking, *The Perfumed Garden*. Other old-Eastern texts wax even more lyrical with talk of the elegant jade hammer or the coral stalk. The Victorians too had their poetic moments with the dart of love and the pleasure pivot, but in more robust mode, they gave us the threatening weapon or truncheon. Keeping for a moment with organs from the past, in British jocular vein we have the upper-crust Honourable Member for Cockshire, the bourgeois Mr John Thomas, and the working class Jolly Roger. In more contemporary parlance, terms for the male member offer a feast of a fry-up or a mixed grill of delights – meat, beef, bacon, sausage, hambone, pork, and salami. Vegetarians will just have to be content with a banana or zucchini (courgette doesn't have the same ring to it somehow and a marrow could be something of a facer). However, for those with a sweet tooth, a jellyroll might be just the thing (again, the Brit equivalent of Swiss roll really won't do), which blues singer Bessie Smith's "kitchen man" had on offer. For those who enjoy outdoor pursuits, there is the middle stump (with reference to the game of cricket) and the tent pole.

Voyeurism This is the term for gaining sexual excitement out of watching others undressing, bathing, in the nude, or engaged in sexual activity. The factor that sets the full-blown, socially undesirable voyeur apart from a rather more healthy interest in observing others in a sexual context is the clandestine, non-consensual nature of the viewing – in other words, peeping Tomism. Sex clubs and sex parties cater for the consensual form of voyeurism, where those of an exhibitionist bent can take active enjoyment out of being watched in action. "Dogging" is another exhibitionist–voyeuristic arrangement. Participants walk their dogs in designated dogging neighbourhoods, and are alerted to the presence of other doggers by the discreet application of signs and symbols to the outside of their homes. Simply ring the bell and watch the show.

Night Visiting Song

The time has come, I can no longer tarry
This morning's tempest I must shortly brave
To cross the moors and high towering mountains
Until I'm in the arms of the one I love.

And when he came to his true love's dwelling
He knelt down gently upon a stane
And whispered softly into the window
"Does my own true love lie there alane?"

She lifted her head from off her down-white pillow
She's lifted the blankets from off her breast
And raised herself up onto an elbow
"Who's that disturbing me from my night's rest?"

"It's I, It's I, It's I, your own true lover
Oh open the door, love and let me in
For I am wet love, and also wearied
For I am wet love, into the skin."

She raised herself up with the greatest of pleasure
She's raised her up and she's let him in
And all night they rolled in each other's arms
Until the long night was past and gone.

And when the long night was past and over
And when the small cocks began to crow
He shook her hand, aye, they've kissed and parted
He's saddled and mounted and away did go.

Traditional song

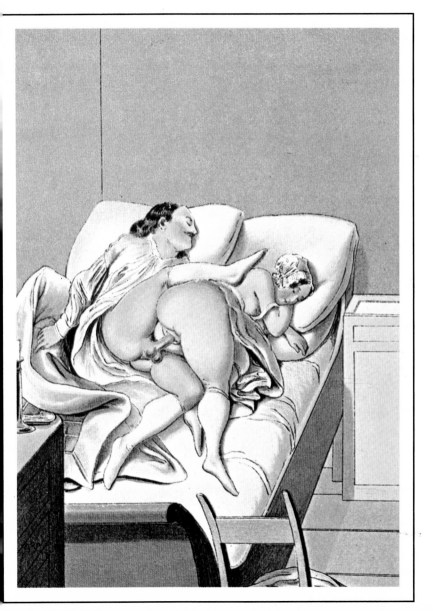

Peter Fendi (1796–1842)

V is for Mount of Venus

Mount of Venus

From *The Way of a Man With A Maid*. The Scarlet Library

"Now in profile, please."

She turned half-round, and now we realized the subtle voluptuousness of Alice's naked figure,

how her exquisitely full and luscious breasts were matched by her somewhat prominent rounded

belly, both in turn being balanced by her glorious fleshy bottom and her fat thighs.

The comparative shortness of her legs only adding piquancy to the whole; while her unusually conspicuous Mount Venus, with its tousle of dark clustering silky hairs, proudly proclaimed itself as the delightful centre of her attractions.

"Thanks, darling!" both Connie and I exclaimed admiringly as we drew her to us and lovingly kissed her, to her evident delight and gratification.

"Now, Connie darling," I said, "I want you to lie down on that couch!" and I removed my arm from her waist to allow her to rise.

"You must do it, darling," I said kindly but firmly as I raised her to her feet. "Come, dear!" and I led her to the couch and made her lie down.

"I must put the straps on you, Connie dear," I said, "because I am sure you won't be able to lie still. Don't be frightened, dear," I added, as I saw a look of terror come over her face. "You are not going to be tortured, or tickled, or hurt, but will be treated most sweetly."

Reluctantly Connie yielded. Quickly Alice attached the straps to her wrists, while I secured the other pair to her ankles; we set the machinery to work and soon she was lying flat on her back, her hands and feet secured to the four corners, the dark-brown upholstery throwing into high relief her lovely figure and dazzling fair hair and skin. I then blindfolded her very carefully in such a way that she could not get rid of the bandage by rubbing her head against the couch.

"Now, Alice dear," I said, "make love to Connie!"

"Oh-h!" cried Connie in shocked surprise, blushing so hotly that even her bosom was suffused with colour. But Alice was already on her knees by Connie's side and was passionately kissing her protesting mouth in the exuberance of her delight at the arrival at last of the much desired opportunity to satisfy on Connie's lovely person, cunt against cunt, her lascivious desires and concupiscence.

I slipped into a chair and took Fanny, who was patiently watching, on my knees, and in sweet companionship we settled ourselves down comfortably to watch Alice make love to Connie. My left arm was round Fanny's waist, the hand toying with the breasts which it could just command, while my right hand played lovingly with her cunt.

With lightly poised hands, Alice touched Connie on the most susceptible parts of herself, her armpits, navel, belly, and especially the soft tender insides of her thighs, evidently reserving for special attention her breasts and cunt. Soon the effect on Connie became apparent, her bosom began to palpitate in sweet agitation, while significant tremors ran through her limbs. "Is it so nice then, darling?" cooed Alice, her eyes dancing with delight as she watched the effect of her operations on Connie's now quivering person; then she rested her hips on Connie's and gently took hold of her breasts.

"Oh Alice!" cried Connie, but Alice closed her lips with her own, half choking her friend with her passionate kisses.

Then raising her head again, she eagerly and delightedly inspected the delicious morsels of Connie's flesh that were imprisoned in her hands. "Oh you darling!" she exclaimed as she squeezed them, "You sweet things!" as she kissed them rapturously. "Oh what dear little nipples!" she cried, taking them in turn into her mouth, her hands all the while squeezing and caressing Connie's lovely breasts till she faintly murmured, "Oh stop, darling!"

"Oh my love! Was I hurting you, darling?" cried Alice with gleaming eyes, as with a smile full of mischief towards us, she reluctantly released Connie's breasts. For a moment she hesitated as if uncertain what next to do, then her eyes rested on Connie's cunt, so sweetly defenceless. An idea seemed to seize her and, with a look of delicious anticipation, she slipped her left arm under Connie's shoulders so as to embrace her, placed her lips on Connie's mouth, extended her right arm, and, without giving Connie the least hint as to her intentions, she placed her hand on Connie's cunt, her slender forefinger resting on the orifice itself.

"Oh-h Alice!" cried Connie, taken completely by surprise and wriggling voluptuously.

"Oh-h Connie!" rapturously murmured Alice, between the hot kisses she was now raining on Connie's mouth, her forefinger beginning to agitate itself inquisitively but lovingly! "Oh darling, your cunny is sweet, sweet!" she murmured as her hand wandered all over Connie's private parts, now stroking and pressing her delicate Mount Venus, now twisting and pulling her hairs, now gently compressing the soft springy flesh between her thumb and forefinger, now passing along the delicate shell-pink lips, and finally gently inserting her finger between them and into the pouting orifice. "I must...I must look at it!" Quickly she withdrew her arm from under Connie's shoulders, gave her a long clinging kiss, then shifted her position by Connie's side, till her head commanded Connie's private parts; then she squared her arms, rested herself on Connie's belly, and with both hands proceeded to examine and study Connie's cunt, her eyes sparkling with delight.

Her curiosity apparently satisfied for the time, Alice raised her head and looked strangely and interrogatively at me. Comprehending her mute enquiry, I smiled and nodded. She smiled back, then dropping her head, she looked intently at Connie's cunt and imprinted a long kiss in its very centre.

Connie squirmed violently. "Oh-h-h!" she ejaculated in a half-strangled voice. With a smile of intense delight, Alice repeated her kiss, then again and again, Connie at each repetition squirming and wriggling in the most delicious way, her vehement plunging telling Alice what flames her hot kisses had aroused in Connie.

Again she opened Connie's cunt, and, keeping its tender lips wide apart, she deposited between them and right inside the orifice itself a long lingering kiss which seemed to set Connie's blood on fire. She glanced merrily at us, her eyes brimming with mischief and delight, then straddled across Connie and arranged herself on her, so that her mouth commanded Connie's cunt, while her stomach rested on Connie's breasts and her cunt lay poised over Connie's mouth, but not touching it. Her legs now lay parallel to Connie's arms and outside them.

Utterly taken aback by Alice's tactics, and in her innocence not recognizing the significance of the position Alice had assumed on her, she cried, "Oh Alice, what are you doing?" Alice grinned delightedly at us, then lowered her head, ran her tongue lightly half a dozen times along the lips of Connie's cunt, and then set to work to gamahuche her.

"Oh-h-h!" shrieked Connie, her voice almost strangled by the violence of the wave of lust that swept over her at the first touch of Alice's tongue. "Oh-h...oh-h-h!" she ejaculated in her utter bewilderment and confusion as she abandoned herself to strangely intoxicating and thrilling sensations hitherto unknown to her, jerking herself madly upwards as if to meet Alice's tongue, her face in her agitated movements coming against Alice's cunt, before it dawned on her confused senses what the warm moist quivering hairy object could be! In wild excitement Alice thoroughly searched Connie's cunt with her active tongue, darting it deeply in, playing delicately on the quivering lips, sucking and tickling her clitoris, and sending Connie into such a state of lust that I thought it wise to intervene...

"Stop, dear!" I called out to Alice, who at once desisted, looking interrogatively at me. "You're trying her too much. Get off her now, dear, and let her recover herself a little or you'll finish her, which we don't want yet." Quickly comprehending the danger, Alice rolled off Connie, turned round, contemplated for a moment Connie's naked wriggling figure, then got onto her again, only this time lips to lips, bubbies against bubbies, and cunt against cunt; she clasped Connie closely to her as she arranged herself, murmuring passionately: "Oh Connie...at last!" then commenced to rub her cunt on Connie's.

"W" is an unashamedly full-bodied letter and so fittingly denotes the female of the species. And here she holds the whip hand both in Woman on top and Whipping itself. If you've still got the energy, try out some Weights on those nipple clamps and head for a Whole-body orgasm.

Woman on Top

There is nothing like the sensation of pinning down your man, taking your turn to pound away while he lies there helpless, at the mercy of your sexual ploys. You can vary the angle of thrust, quicken and slow the pace to play out the pleasure, or subtly tease his penis by squeezing with your PC muscle. He can work your buttocks, pulling your weight up and down on his penis – especially when you begin to tire – or finger your anus. Or you can choose to keep him fully under your control, bearing down on his arms. I don't mean to spoil the fun, but if you have long hair, it's worth pinning it back or up since, once drenched with sweat, it clings in an unhelpful manner over both your faces.

WAM WAM stands for "wet and messy", which can mean either getting yourself or someone else wet and messy by way of sexual gratification, but not, in any case, with the aid of bodily fluids. And why not? It's all good, clean…well, good fun anyway. As well as having a strong following, the sport actually has a lengthy heritage – think of the tradition of mud-wrestling (more likely Jello-wrestling if you're Stateside) or that old stag party stalwart, the wet T-shirt competition. But there are choices to be made before you get down to the messy business itself. Is your preference to be naked for the event, or would the buzz come from being all dressed-up or perhaps in a fetish outfit such as a nurse's uniform? What about context? Is it a private revelling just between the two of you, a romp among like-minded friends, or an orchestrated event in a public situation? And what's the chosen messy substance to be, bearing in mind the clean-up operation. Methycellulose – a thickening agent used in milkshakes, among other things – is billed as the best, but vegetable oil, paint, or chocolate may have more appeal.

Wet Dreams It is perhaps significant that what was traditionally known as a wet dream is now termed a "nocturnal emission". This may be technically rather more *à point* but it does miss out one important facet – the dream. In the case of pubescent males, wet dreams may be a physical imperative due to a build-up of semen unrelieved by other outlets, yet even in these instances, the "emission" is often accompanied, if not triggered, by an erotic dream. And if we are still in doubt as to the extent of the role played by the subconscious, we might consider the fact that adult men also have wet dreams, albeit not on such a frequent basis as adolescents, and so do women. For boys, a wet dream is often their first experience of orgasm, while it is reputed that women rarely have a "wet dream" before having had an orgasm in one of the more conventional ways. All this nicely dovetails with the psychic and spiritual aspects of sexual gratification explored by the ancient Eastern and Native American traditions, which have gained much currency in recent times.

Whipping If being Madam/Master Whiplash is your and your partner's sexual ambition, you need the right tools for the job, a considered approach, and a practised technique. This will also aid safety. Accomplished "handlers" use a range of whips gradually increasing in impact, from small and soft to start the release of "feel-good" and pain-dulling endorphins, to the longer, more heavy-duty jobs as the pain threshold rises. Certain suppliers specialize in whips specifically designed for SM use. Balance is all-important, with the handle, traditionally woven leather, weighted relative to the weight and length of the tails. At the softer end of the latter are velvet, woven fabrics, deer skin, and fur, moving up to various weights of leather, horsehair, and rubber. The buttocks are a relatively safe area for whipping; the kidneys, abdomen, and spine must always be avoided.

Wilmot, John, Earl of Rochester Rochester stood out as a colourful character even by the considerably colourful standards of the court of Charles II following the end of Puritan dominance and the restoration of the monarchy in England in 1660. But in spite of his notoriously dissolute existence, he was a seriously good satirical poet, second only in standing to Dryden in his day. Much of his output, however, was, although highly accomplished, downright pornographic (one such poem was entitled "Signior Dildo"), which he penned for an "underground" audience of fellow debauchees. It wasn't until after his death that the bulk of his writings were ascribed to him and properly published. One of the madcap incidents that set the tenor of his life was when, as a young man, he tried unsuccessfully to abduct the beautiful and witty heiress Elizabeth Malet following her money-grabbing relatives' opposition to Rochester marrying her (which he finally did two years later). He had to cool his heels in the Tower for a few weeks before the King forgave him. Having subsequently been banished from court, Rochester set himself up in practice as "Dr Bendo" – a physician specializing in barrenness.

Ray Leaning (www.leaning.co.uk)

Mock Song

"I swive as well as others do;
I'm young, not yet deformed;
My tender heart, sincere and true,
Deserves not to be scorned.
Why, Phyllis, then, why will you swive
With forty lovers more?"
"Can I," said she, "with nature strive?
*Alas I am, alas I am a **whore**!"*

"Were all my body larded o'er
With darts of love, so thick
That you might find in every pore
A well-stuck standing prick,
Whilst yet my eyes alone were free,
My heart would never doubt,
In amorous rage and ecstasy,
To wish those eyes, to wish those eyes fucked out."

John Wilmot, Earl of Rochester (1647–1680)

Peter Fendi (1796–1842)

W is for Wet

Wet Wet Wet

Christine Pountney

I have recently taken up swimming again at my local leisure centre. I'm a good swimmer and over the last few weeks have increased in strength and speed. The other day I actually hit a young man in the face while passing him in the opposite direction. I didn't do it intentionally, of course, and managed to gurgle a bubbly "Sorry" as I continued on my way, but eventually he moved into a slower lane.

In retrospect, this may have done something in the way of singling me out to people who, unbeknownst to me, had their eye on me. People who belong to a secret society of nocturnal swimmers that I want to tell you about.

What I am about to describe only happened to me once. I've never seen them since, nor will I ever, in all likelihood, see them again. That is my only regret.

But for now, all I will say is that I had begun to notice my own growing complicity in a kind of aquatic pecking order. It had also begun to dawn on me that swimming in a public pool is a lot like flirting in a public house. There is a strict but unspoken protocol, a natural migration of people into smaller more compatible groups, ways of getting closer to the object of your curiosity and arousal, and ways of putting distance in between, or even eliminating the competition.

Hypnotized by the repetition and exertion of my own muscular movements, I would often become aware of the other bodies only as electrical currents, like strip lights passing in a tunnel. Occasionally, a leg would brush my own or a hand claw at my waist, sometimes noticeably enough to arouse my curiosity concerning the author of these gestures. This is when the flirting would begin. Packaged as innocuously as a beneficial physical activity, people often overlook the extent to which swimming provides the perfect opportunity for voyeurism. It is almost impossible, when following close on the heels of another swimmer, not to perform an intimate inspection of their body. How could a man not enjoy watching the hourglass shape of a woman's gusset bisecting her body as, ass high up in the water, her long legs keep flying open like springs? And how could a woman, feeling a man approaching her from behind, not resist parting her legs even wider while doing the breast stroke, only to feel a deliciously achy sensation deep within her anus every time she reaches out with her toes?

There was a day not long ago when I was sure I was being followed. When I sped up, the man behind me did too, effortlessly, and yet he never passed me either. I could almost feel the heat of his body when, crowded together at the end of the lane, I would slow down to somersault. Pushing off the wall with my feet, I would practically have to swim underneath him as I angled over to the other side. I could feel his eyes caressing my skin and, after a while, I actually began to feel sexually excited by his proximity, by the bullying, intrusive way he had of following so close behind.

It was almost like fucking. Lap after exhausting lap, every time I pulled my arms in, scooping water into my chest then snapping straight as an arrow and surging forward, I could imagine him penetrating me.

And all the while, right there in front of me, as if I was just another link in a long chain of bodies, swam the vision of a plump but sturdy woman, breasts pushed out to the sides, thighs rippling like cream, the dark line of her burgundy bathing suit not more than two inches wide across her vulva. She was a strong swimmer, and as I followed her, I too felt as if I was chasing her, trying to get close enough to flick a finger under her gusset, pull it aside, and slip my tongue into her wet sex.

When I got out of the pool I was flushed and delirious. I walked slowly to the changing room, regal as a drunk and long-forgotten beauty queen, the lactic acid already stiffening my muscles from the effort I'd made, my whole body pulsing and tingling with adrenalin.

I got under the shower head and closed my eyes. When I opened them, the woman I'd been swimming behind was standing beside me with her bathing suit pulled down around her waist, soaping her breasts.

"Hi," she nodded.

"Hi," I said back, watching her lean against the shower button. "You know, if you screw the knob to the right, the shower stays on and you don't have to keep pressing it."

"Thanks," she said and smiled. "My name's Kate, by the way."

"I'm Shalla," I said and held out my hand. The next time I saw her she was standing just outside the leisure centre. I had been for a swim, showered, and was heading home. She was standing on the curb outside the building with a man around the same age. She was wearing a thick army-green parka with a fur-lined hood and a bright green backpack that matched her eyes. The man she was with was tall and handsome and had a strong jaw like an all-American male model. He was wearing a jean jacket and a pair of jeans and carrying a brown bag slung across his chest.

"Shalla," she said. "I want you to meet Dean."

"Hi Dean," I said, shaking his warm hand. He didn't seem to want to let go of it.

"We were waiting for you. We wanted to give you this," she said. "We hope you can come." Then she leaned forward and kissed me on the cheek. Dean did the same and then they were off.

I looked down at the envelope she had given me. It was made of purple card, the texture of handmade paper. I opened it and pulled out a gold square with black writing. Bordered by mermaids on either side, the following was written:

Let the secret society of underwater lovemakers drench you with pleasure on the next full moon.
By personal invitation only.

I stared at the invitation in disbelief and yet, at the same time, my heart began to beat wildly.

Over the next few days, the moon waxed into a pale round face and then it was time. I dressed carefully and put my swimsuit in a bag, although I wasn't sure I was going to need it. Outside, the night was cold and starry, backyards and parking lots looked eerie and exposed in the moon's silver gleam.

When I got to the leisure centre, it looked completely deserted. For a moment I felt like I'd been duped and a wave of humiliation washed over me. Then the door opened slowly, and a man holding a candle beckoned me inside, his elongated shadow flickering on the ceiling.

"Come on in," he said, closing the door behind me. "I'm afraid I'm going to have to ask you to give me everything you're wearing before you go in."

"What?" I asked.

"Don't worry. This isn't a trick," he said and opened the door to what usually served as the reception office. The room was filled with neat little piles of clothing, all tagged and organized, sitting on top of bags and pairs of shoes. "Everyone's equal beyond this point," he said.

"But you're not undressed," I said.

"That's because I'm the doorman."

"Right," I said and took a deep breath and handed him my bag and began to undress. When I bent over to pull my underwear off the ends of my feet, he reached out and ran a hand over my ass. I stood up and he bent forward and kissed my breasts, sucking on each nipple before straightening up and pointing me towards a door.

"That way lies paradise," he said and gave me a little push.

I gave him one final look, then walked across the hall and through a door. A row of candles were arranged on the floor creating a pathway I assumed I should follow. My body was now alight with an irresistible curiosity, which was magnetically pulling me forward. I could feel the doorman's saliva drying on my nipples, and the cool linoleum beneath my bare feet. I padded softly down the hall following the murmur of sighs coming from around the corner.

The trail of candles ended just in front of the men's locker room. The door was propped open and steam was curling around the doorjamb and spiralling slowly in the light. I ventured forwards and in the shadows all around me I thought I could discern a few slow, undulating shapes, a man's arm and shoulder, bulging with muscles and glistening with sweat, a head of wet hair thrown back and slapped across a woman's pale back. There were a few more candles burning in the room, barely enough to see by, and I could hear the hissing of the showers. I groped my way towards them and, as I got closer, the steam became so dense it was like fog. I stood at the edge of the tiles, feeling the wisps of heat like tongues on my skin. Someone tapped me on the shoulder and I turned to see Dean's smiling face.

"Hi there," he said.

"Hi Dean," I said, grateful for the familiarity of his face. He took my hand and put it on his erection.

"Do you want to take a shower?" he whispered, nuzzling my neck.

He turned me around and held me under the hot water, then pivoted the shower head so it was aimed at the wall and pushed me into the spray. He held me sideways against the wall with a forearm braced across my shoulders and prodded me with his cock, rubbing the tip forwards along my cunt to my clitoris and back again. Before I could make sense of what was going on, he was bending me over and entering me from behind as smoothly as a diver hitting the water. He pushed me so far forwards that I had to reach a hand out to steady myself and found myself touching a woman's back.

She was on her knees giving a man a blow-job, but when she felt my hands on her shoulders, she turned around, raised her chest to my face, and put a breast in my mouth. Then she crawled underneath me, and while I leaned on her buttocks, she put her tongue next to Dean's penis and licked my clitoris. I reached around her ass and slipped my fingers

into her cunt, while the man who she'd been sucking straddled her, grabbed me, and put his dick in my mouth.

For the next few minutes we were like a well-oiled machine, rising and falling, pulling and jerking and tensing and thrusting in unison. Just as I was about to come, Dean pulled out abruptly and said, "Let's go for a swim. I don't want to come just yet. It's good to wait – and you. You're driving me crazy, baby." Dazed and breathless, I followed him to the pool area where what seemed like a hundred naked bodies were writhing in and out of the water, silver and glistening in the moonlight which poured in like skimmed milk through a skylight in the ceiling. "Who are all these people?" I whispered to Dean.

"You'd never guess," he said and led me to the water's edge. As soon as I had slipped into the pool, a dozen pairs of hands were on my body, smothering my skin, probing every orifice, a finger in my mouth, another in my anus. Dean had disappeared and I was trapped in a bramble of anonymous limbs. I couldn't fight the collective strength of their avid caresses and decided to give myself over to the sensation. Suddenly, however, someone was pushing me underwater. I struggled to free myself but was held down. A man positioned himself underneath me and penetrated me. Hands were released and I came up gasping for breath. The man who was inside me was in front of me now, holding my legs around his waist, while another man, standing behind him, was penetrating him. This man was clutching my hips, sandwiching the man who was inside me. This man was looking over my shoulder at a man who had come up behind and gently penetrated my ass.

I have never been penetrated by two men at once and my whole pelvic area felt tight and on fire. I was held in place so tightly that I couldn't move and yet all around me these strong male bodies were slowly pumping and grinding. And then all of a sudden, as if on cue, we plunged underwater again. I was held down for what seemed like forever – 30, 40 seconds. I began to fight for breath and yet I couldn't deny the exquisite sensation of skin rubbing against skin, of a cock in my cunt and one in my ass, sliding in and out.

Just when I was resigned to an ecstatic death by drowning, we resurfaced and the moment I sucked air into my lungs, my whole lower body began to contract with the most powerful orgasm I have ever had. Urged on by my cries, the men continued to fuck me, harder at first and then slowing considerately as my breathing began to slow down too. Then they swam off in search of other prey and I was left alone, holding the edge of the pool, floating on my back. Someone approached me and kissed me lightly on the shoulder. "Shalla, it's me, Kate."

"Oh, god, Kate, am I ever happy to see you." She put her mouth on mine and dragged me underwater…To this day, I have never seen her again. Or Dean, for that matter, who was so kind to me. He found me later that night, asleep on a bench under a towel. "You must be tired," he said. "Can we take you home?" I nodded and he escorted me to the door. He kissed me goodnight and left me with the doorman, who helped me get dressed again. When he opened the door, daylight was breaking and there was a car waiting. The doorman put me in the back seat and told the driver to take me home. He even knew my address but I was too exhausted to question him.

On the way home, I had a fleeting wish that my driver would stop in a dark alley and rape me in the back, but he too was a gentleman to the end and even waited until I had closed my front door before driving away.

This short story first appeared in The Erotic Review *(see page 319).*

"X" means "sex"; it's as plain as that. Its shape is the very embodiment of bedroom bondage — the spread-eagled figure tied to the bedposts. It's also the warning signal in X-rated of "adult" material, we hope of a sexual nature, as well as the defining sign of the female sex. And let's not forget those X-ray specs — the subject of every schoolboy's wet dreams.

X Chromosome

Cast your mind back to the classroom and you may recall that the X chromosome is considered to be the female one out of the two sex chromosomes, normal females having a whole two X chromosomes all to themselves – one activated and one for back-up. Males have only one X and a smaller Y chromosome, and it's the latter that puts into action the development of male characteristics. But that's the one small difference in the genetic make-up of the sexes; otherwise, we have 22 out of the 23 pairs of chromosomes in common. And because we all have one X, it's the chromosome with all the genes essential to growth and body function. Y just concerns itself with developing testes etc., but it has now been discovered that X is even in on the act in sperm production. It's no wonder that many of us feel ourselves to be somewhere on a continuum in terms of our sexual and gender identity.

Xenophilia

Used in a sexual context, this term denotes being sexually excited by strangers. One may say who isn't, but, as with most sexual peccadilloes, it's all a matter of degree. The film featured in the following entry, *Last Tango in Paris*, is a case in point. Here, the mutual attraction of the leading couple was largely fuelled by the individuals' protection of their own anonymity. However, it was the Marlon Brando character's breaking of the faith of this "agreement" that led to the fatal denouement – she shot him. A less hazardous way to toy with at least the concept of the unknown is to use a blindfold and play a little mind game with your partner. In this way, you can safely explore the excitement of the imagined new and the accompanying thrill of detachment.

X-Rated

The old X-rating of movies, while generally applied to what by today's standards would mostly be judged shy of softcore, was enough to set the pulses racing with just the promise of silver screen sex. As the '60s rolled on, increasing amounts of sexual shenanigans were to be enjoyed under the guise of humour in, for example, the very British *Carry On* films – those masterpieces of the double entendre – and Russ "King of the Nudies" Meyer's sexploitative comedies. But in more serious vein, the tail end of the decade proved something of a censorial watershed with the strangely titled *I Am Curious – Yellow*, a quasi-documentary Swedish film containing explicit sex scenes, and *The Killing of Sister George*, whose shock value was earned by its lesbian lovemaking content. Added to which, *Midnight Cowboy* became the only X-rated movie to be Academy Awarded Best Picture, before all hell broke loose with the arrival of *Deep Throat* in 1972. *Last Tango in Paris* made its not inconsiderable splash the same year. Starring the maturing Marlon Brando alongside the tender and then unknown Maria Schneider, the movie majors on their brief, emotionally staccato relationship, which almost entirely unfolds within the confines of a Parisian apartment. Not only did it feature sex play with sadomasochistic undertones

but an anal sex sequence, with the household butter making a novelty appearance as the "lube" of the day. The latter scene was cut in the British version and the Italian authorities went ape over it, handing the director Bertolucci a four-month prison sentence in addition to banning the movie.

X is for X-Rated

The Show

From *Forum* magazine

Outside, the city was a night sky of square stars: a galaxy of windows, a constellation of consumers among flashing, pulsing advertisements — product-placement nebulae.

Smoke was standing, a rectangular sun of a different type, looking out at the spectacle of night time New York. He felt like he should be sneering, thinking something arrogant – like how he, behind this one window, wasn't just another sun, but rather a media prank nova ready to blast the consumer galaxy of NYC with mind-blowing light. Yeah, something like that. Instead, he was really thinking was how his new boots – nice though they were – were really killing his feet, that he only had $17.15 in his checking account…and that he was really worried about Jayne.

"Well, the Master has worked his magic," Truck said from where he was sprawled in a far corner of the tiny Times Square apartment, circuit board in his lap, a faint plume of grey smoke rising from the soldering iron in one hand. "All he needs now is for the talent to do its thing."

Meaning Smoke and Jayne. "Give it a rest, will ya?" Smoke said, still looking out the window at the busy drones of NYC.

"Hey, man, just laying it out, that's all. We've only got a day or so before someone notices my expert hacks. We've really got to do this thing and get the hell out before then."

The apartment wasn't even seedy. Beside the one window, it was just a stained sink under a flaking mirror, a tiny press board night stand, a (non-working) wall sconce shaped like a seashell, and the bed. The mattress was way too soft, like lying on a decaying marshmallow, and the piss-coloured bedspread smelled of ancient cigarettes and mildew.

The atmosphere wasn't why they were there. "I got it, I got it," Smoke said, running a thin hand through his long, dark hair. He sighed. "But I can't force her or anything, man."

"Didn't ask you to – just stating the facts, is all. Wouldn't want my beautiful work to go to waste, you know."

Running through the interior wall was a special trunk line – part of the Tyrano-Vision screen overlooking Times Square's control system. The circuit board in Truck's lap was patched skullduggerously into it — linking the tiny solid-state camera duct-taped to the wall directly to the 80-foot monster screen. Their first act of "awareness terrorism" – as they called it – had been to alter some dozen or so billboards throughout Manhattan, turning cigarette ads to GOT CANCER? After that, they'd placed OUT OF DISORDER stickers on hundreds of vending machines all over the island. It was just Smoke, Truck, and Jayne – but they'd made the *Daily News*, *The Times*, and all kinds of local TV stations. Today, though, or better yet tonight, was going to be their *coup de grace*: a skilful manipulation of corporate propaganda to bring their message to the milling throngs of Times Square – an artistic assault on the plastic culture imposed at dollar-point on the people of New York:

Smoke and Jayne, 80 feet tall, fucking on the Tyrano-Vision screen.

A "shave and a haircut" knock brought Smoke from the window to the scarred and battered door. Jayne stood, looking sheepish and small despite her Army Surplus jacket, and black parachute pants, in the hall.

There was just one problem – and it wasn't with Truck's hackwork. "I'm going to check the jumpers on the roof again," he said, carefully putting the circuit board aside. "Let me know if you guys get that romantic spark going." He slipped past Jayne and vanished towards the back stairs.

Jayne stepped in, closing the door behind her. "Just call me frigid," she said with a wry smile, slipping off her glasses and dropping them on to the bed.

Smoke put his arms around her. "Fuck that," he said with a smile. "You do what you want to do – you just don't want to do it. It's cool."

She shook her head. Jayne wasn't a small slip, she was full-bodied and outrageous – or, at least, normally outrageous. Her face was puckish, her lips and eyes set on "perpetually amused", and her body language usually broadcasted "fuck with me if you dare"; but right then she was smaller, drained, and shy, and "perpetually amused" seemed more like "sad self-deprecation".

Smoke felt something down deep, an ache at seeing the transformation. He liked his wild Jayne, his Jayne who liked to fuck on the subway, who liked to walk around his scummy little West Side apartment, proudly nude. He liked to hear her mumble when they made out, telling him in explicit detail what she wanted to do, was going to do to him, with him. It was only because of Outrageous Jayne that the Times Square prank was even considered – and she'd seemed all for it. In fact, she seemed more than all for it for weeks, until, that is, the day before, when Outrageous Jayne, the Jayne who liked to flash her plump tits at passing tour buses, had come down with a severe case of…shyness?

"It's just…I don't know," Jayne said, pushing herself back into Smoke's thin arms. "I'm nervous, that's all – and it freaks me out."

"Doing it?" Doing it in front of a thousand strangers. "Or being nervous?"

"Both, I guess," she said, turning carefully around until her lips were just about even with Smoke's. "It's weird – and I don't like it."

Smoke didn't say anything – instead he just bent down and kissed her. Jayne was wearing her favourite lipstick, Urban Decay, and the familiar heavy slickness of her lips on his made Smoke's breathing start to come fast and quick.

"Whatever turns you on," Smoke said, slowly drawing his lips across hers, "or doesn't is cool with me. Okay, babe?"

"Yeah," she said, her voice sad and heavy.

She put her face down on to Smoke's chest. His FUCK THE FUCKERS T-shirt was barely clean but that was good, because Jayne could relax into its comfortable smell, sagging just a bit in his arms. "I know. But I really wanted to, you know? I've been thinking of nothing else for the last few days. "Up here" she said, pulling an arm free to tap her forehead "it really gets me going. The idea of all those people watching us, getting turned on while we do it – oh, man, but something gets caught down here." She shifted her finger down between her plump breasts. "It gets stuck somehow, gets all mixed up. I don't know what to do."

"You do whatever you want to do, babe. Don't worry about Truck or me – fuck, what's more important? Screwing with the people out there or doing what you want to do? We can fuck with them any time – it's you that's really important.'

"Thanks," she said in a sweet little voice, a little girl's tones from the young woman's full mouth. She kissed him again, from gentle to a slow, hot dance of firm tongues. "I want to – I'm just scared," she said, breaking the kiss long enough to say it.

"Yeah, I know." Smoke knew he should have been all caring and shit, but his body wasn't listening. A hard cock wasn't really "caring", but it didn't seem to care: in his battered, threadbare jeans his dick felt like another arm, one that throbbed towards Jayne. "It would have been fun, wouldn't it?"

"Oh, yeah," Jayne said, running a finger around where his nipples made small tents in his T-shirt. "All those people down there, looking up at us. I'm such a freak – but it really gets me going."

Smoke returned the gesture, opening her jacket and circling her nipples with his fingertips, but Jayne responded with a greater gesture – the tents that appeared on her own T-shirt were five times larger, and much more sensitive: she arched her back against Smoke's methodical circles, and her eyes glazed over slightly. "Me, too."

"I've been thinking about it a lot," Jayne said as Smoke pushed her heavy jacket off her shoulders. It fell to the ugly yellow carpet with a heavy fabric impact. "How we'd start by just standing there, up on the screen, just the two of us…naked. Oh."

The thought but also Smoke lifting her T-shirt up and placing a single, firm kiss to her left nipple made her voice trail off. But her voice and words returned as he gave the same treatment to her right. "You'd be hard. Oh, yeah, hard like you are now, right? Fucking hard: cock all big and pretty. Bobbing up and down just a bit, maybe even a little bit of come at the tip. Just the way I like it." As she spoke, Jayne rubbed her hand down the front of Smoke's jeans, playing with the fat bulge, tracing the outline of his hard cock. "Just the two of us, 80 feet high, naked, hard and..."

"Wet?" Smoke said, lifting her shirt up and off. As it finally passed over her head he leaned forward and kissed her, long and firmly.

"Very," Outrageous Jayne said, smiling. "Very wet. I wish I could be like those porno girls. You know, with pussy juice dripping down my legs. But, well, what the fuck, why not? Okay, there we are, standing there, 80 feet tall, your cock all nice and really fucking hard, and me, pussy juice making my thighs all wet and shiny..."

She stopped as Smoke pulled off his own shirt, then bent forward to kiss, then suck, at her firmly erect nipples. Her breasts were full, plump – white, but not pale – and they jiggled slightly as Smoke worked his lips around the so-soft skin and directly on the brown nipples.

As he broke the kiss, the suck, she continued, "Yeah, 80 feet tall. People would look up and stare at us, look at us, up there, very hard and wet. They'd stare, stare at us. Maybe a cab would crash, the guy not looking where he was going. Guys would get all hard, their cocks tight in their pants. Some chicks would get wet, and their nipples really hard. But some would be all shocked and shit, and try not to look, but you know they would, 'cause their cocks and cunts would be all hard and wet, too."

Shoes, pants on the floor. Then Smoke, too. Like in her story, she was wet, though her juice

didn't paint her thighs, at least not yet, and he was very, very hard. "Then we'd start to kiss, and touch each other. You'd grab my tits. Oh, yeah" her voice quavered as Stone did just that "and I'd wrap my hand around your cock, and slowly jerk you off."

A little bead of pre-come had dotted the head of Smoke's cock, and Jayne spread it over the tip, the head, and the shaft. There wasn't a lot, but there was enough to make him slippery enough. Smiling down at the dick in her hand, she smiled, eyes dancing over all the details of him. "And they'd be so hard, so wet down there, watching us. Maybe a guy would start to jerk off: taking his little weenie out of his pants and beating off looking up at us on that big fucking screen. Maybe some chick would grab her tits, pulling at her nipples." Jayne did the same, smiling wickedly at Smoke.

Smoke smiled back, feeling his heart hammering in his chest. Reaching out, he softly petted her shaven mons, enjoying – as he always enjoyed – the soft pebbled feel of her most recent shave. Without a word, Jayne spread her legs, allowing two of his fingers to go between and up, parting her lips.

"Then I'd suck your cock. I'd get down on my 80-feet-tall knees and take your dick in my mouth and start to suck you off...and all those people down there, they'd all watch and they'd all start to moan. Maybe a couple of them, some freaks like us, or maybe some straights who just couldn't take it any more, would start to do it – sucking and fucking like us."

Like in her narrative, Jayne lowered herself to the dirty carpet. Kneeling, facing Smoke's long cock, she stroked it a few more times. Then, smiling, she kissed the tip, tasting salt and bitter pre-come. "Maybe a couple of dykes, too, would get down there on the street. Skirts all pulled up, panties pushed aside, they'd eat each other's pussies, chowing down on sweet muff in the middle of Times Square. Nasty little fag boys, too. They'd get down on each other and start sucking cock, then swallowing come as they all watched me take you in my mouth, down my throat."

Then she put actions to words, carefully opening her mouth and easing Smoke's cock into her and then, inch by inch, down her throat. It was a familiar game for both of them, so Smoke knew to spread his legs and push his cock down just a bit and Jayne knew to tilt her head just so.

Time stretched out, and the world shrank. Smoke knew he should say something to keep the game going but his vocabulary drained out of him, whole classifications of words with each inch of his cock down Jayne's throat. Still, he loved Jayne, and so he tried his best. "Oh, yeah, they'd watch us. They'd watch us fuck and suck each other. The guys would be so hard, the women all wet. They'd do it with us. Fuck and suck each other as we did on the big picture."

They'd been together long enough, had done it enough, that Jayne knew when Smoke was coming close to…coming…so she pulled away, smiling up at the joy on his face. "Let me," she said, stroking him a few times. "I think I'm better at this, babe." She lost herself in Smoke's cock for a minute. "Yeah, we'd fuck for them. We'd make their days, their weeks, their years – they'd talk about us forever, how they'd seen us up there on that big screen. We'd be in their dreams. They'd fantasize about us, they'd jerk off to us, fuck people but think about us…for years."

As Jayne stroked him, she reached her hand around to his firm little arse and carefully hunted for his arsehole. Ringing it with a fingertip, she continued. "We'd fuck our ways into their heads, stud. We'd screw our ways into their dreams…"

In its capital form, the letter "Y" is highly suggestive of the union of the female and male genitalia, with its pubic-shaped upper impaled on an upstanding shaft. What could be more appropriate for the mystical conjunction of Yin and Yang and the symbol of the sacred vulva, the Yoni?

Yin and Yang

The ancient Chinese philosophy of yin and yang is all about the balancing and union of opposites – which equals mind-blowing sex! Yin is feminine and yang is masculine, but that's not the same as yin is woman and yang is man – no thinking this venerable could be that straightforward. Women have some yang characteristics but yin is dominant, and men vice versa. The theory goes that if we allow our primary traits to overpower our secondary traits, or if she has depleted her yin stocks and him his yang, sexual nirvana (to mix philosophies) is a non-starter.

The Yellow Book

Not a book but a magazine, which first brought the infamous English illustrator, Aubrey Beardsley, to fame. The artist's challenging of the conventions of the day (the latter quarter of the 19th century) was already in evidence in his first artistic assignment – an extensive series of illustrations for an edition of Malory's *Morte d'Arthur*. Among the many artworks that didn't directly relate to the text, various satyrs and other "unseemly" figures popped up, all in mock-Medieval-cum-pre-Raphaelite style. Following an article publicizing him and his work, Beardsley was commissioned to illustrate the English version of Oscar Wilde's scandalous play of sex and vice, *Salome*. It wasn't only Wilde who was less than ecstatic over the results, although that may well have been because the artist was up to his old tricks of upstaging the author, not to mention sending him up with the inclusion of the odd caricature. Even the pioneering publisher, John Lane, found a few of the drawings too rich for his, or his readership's, blood. But the quality of his work was such that Beardsley was sought out to be art editor of a new provocative periodical on art and literature, *The Yellow Book*, the livery deliberately chosen to echo the racy yellow-bound French novels. The journal was a success, despite its denouncement by the critics as obscene, but Beardsley's role came to a crashing end when Wilde was arrested in 1895 with what the press reported to be a copy of *The Yellow Book* tucked under his arm.

Yoni : Before the male sex organ took over and subsequently dominated throughout most of Western history as a symbol of fertility and an object of worship, the yoni – or vulva – was the holy of holies. Images of the yoni have been found in caves in the South of France dating back 30,000 years. In the East, the pre-Hindu worship of the Goddess featured the ceremonial honouring of the yoni. The stylized representation of the female pubic area as a downward-pointing triangle is one that appears across diverse cultures in different ages.

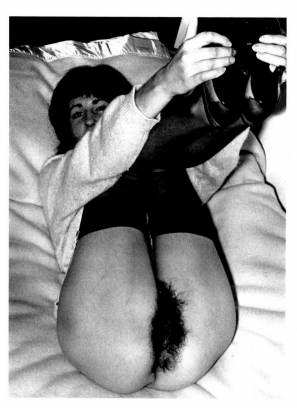

Eric Wilkins (Contemporary)

Aubrey Beardsley (1872–1898)

The Vine

I dreamed this mortal part of mine
Was metamorphosed to a vine;
Which crawling one and every way
Enthralled my dainty Lucia.
Methought her long small legs and thighs
I with my tendrils did surpise;
Her belly, buttocks, and her waist
By my soft nervelets we embraced:
About her head I writhing hung,
And with rich clusters (hid among
The leaves) her temples I behung,
So that my Lucia seemed to me
Young Bacchus *ravished by his tree.*
My curls about her neck did crawl,
And arms and hands they did enthral:
So that she could not freely stir
(All parts there made one prisoner).
But when I crept with leaves to hide
Those parts which maids keep unespied,
Such fleeting pleasures there I took
That with the fancy I awoke;
And found (ah me!) this flesh of mine
More like a stock than a vine.

Robert Herrick (1591–1674)

Peter Fendi (1796–1842)

Y. is for Yoni

About women acting the part of a man; and of the work of a man

From Chapter 8 of the *Kama Sutra of Vatsyayana*

When a woman sees that her lover is fatigued by constant congress, without having his desire satisfied, she should, with his permission, lay him down upon his back, and give him assistance by acting his part. She may also do this to satisfy the curiosity of her lover, or her own desire of novelty.

There are two ways of doing this, the first is when during congress she turns round, and gets on the top of her lover, in such a manner as to continue the congress, without obstructing the pleasure of it; and the other is when she acts the man's part from the beginning. At such a time, with flowers in her hair hanging loose, and her smiles broken by hard breathings, she should press upon her lover's bosom with her own breasts, and lowering her head frequently, should do in return the same actions which he used to do before, returning his blows and chaffing him, should say, "I was laid down by you, and fatigued with hard congress, I shall now therefore lay you down in return." She should then again manifest her own bashfulness, her fatigue, and her desire of stopping the congress. In this way she should do the work of a man, which we shall presently relate.

Whatever is done by a man for giving pleasure to a woman is called the work of a man, and is as follows:

While the woman is lying on his bed, and is as it were abstracted by his conversation, he should loosen the knot of her undergarments, and when she begins to dispute with him, he should overwhelm her with kisses. Then when his lingam is erect he should touch her with his hands in various places, and gently manipulate various parts of the body. If the woman is bashful, and if it is the first time that they have come together, the man should place his hands between her thighs, which she would probably keep close together, and if she is a very young girl, he should first get his hands upon her breasts, which she would probably cover with her own hands, and under her armpits and on her neck. If, however, she is a seasoned woman, he should do whatever is agreeable either to him or to her, and whatever is fitting for the occasion. After this he should take hold of her hair, and hold her chin in his fingers for the purpose of kissing her. On this, if she is a young girl, she will become bashful and close her eyes. Anyhow he should gather from the action of the woman what things would be pleasing to her during congress.

Here Suvarnanabha says that while a man is doing to the woman what he likes best during congress, he should always make a point of pressing those parts of her body on which she turns her eyes.

The signs of the enjoyment and satisfaction of the woman are as follows: her body relaxes, she closes her eyes, she puts aside all bashfulness, and shows increased willingness to unite the two organs as closely together as possible. On the other hand, the signs of her want of enjoyment and of failing to be satisfied are as follows: she shakes her hands, she does not let the man get up, feels dejected, bites the man, kicks him, and continues to go on moving after the man has finished. In such cases the man should rub the yoni of the woman with his hand and fingers (as the elephant rubs anything with his trunk) before engaging in congress, until it is softened, and after that is done he should proceed to put his lingam into her.

The acts to be done by the man are:

Moving forward

Friction or churning

Piercing

Rubbing

Pressing

Giving a blow

The blow of a boar

The blow of a bull

The sporting of a sparrow.

When the organs are brought together properly and directly it is called "moving the organ forward".

When the lingam is held with the hand, and turned all round in the yoni, it is called "churning".

When the yoni is lowered, and the upper part of it is struck with the lingam, it is called "piercing".

When the same thing is done on the lower part of the yoni, it is called "rubbing".

When the yoni is pressed by the lingam for a long time, it is called "pressing".

When the lingam is removed to some distance from the yoni, and then forcibly strikes it, it is called "giving a blow".

When only one part of the yoni is rubbed with the lingam, it is called the "blow of a boar".

When both sides of the yoni are rubbed in this way, it is called the "blow of a bull".

When the lingam is in the yoni, and moved up and down frequently, and without being taken out, it is called the "sporting of a sparrow". This takes place at the end of congress.

When a woman acts the part of a man, she has the following things to do in addition to the nine given above:

The pair of tongs

The top

The swing.

When the woman holds the lingam in her yoni, draws it in, presses it, and keeps it thus in her for a long time, it is called the "pair of tongs".

When, while engaged in congress, she turns round like a wheel, it is called the "top". This is learnt by practice only.

When the man lifts up the middle part of his body, and the woman turns round her middle part, it is called the "swing".

When the woman is tired, she should place her forehead on that of her lover, and should thus take rest without disturbing the union of the organs, and when the woman has rested herself the man should turn round and begin the congress again.

There are also some verses on the subject as follows:

"Though a woman is reserved, and keeps her feelings concealed; yet when she gets on the top of a man, she then shows all her love and desire. A man should gather from the actions of the woman of what disposition she is, and in what way she likes to be enjoyed. A woman during her monthly courses, a woman who has been lately confined, and a fat woman should not be made to act the part of a man."

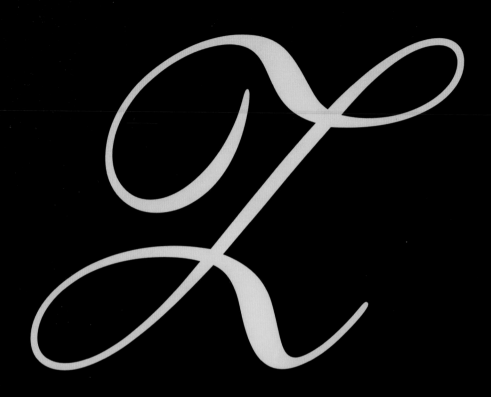

Just when you thought you would be draining the last dregs from the loving cup, get ready for some rearguard action in the form of the "zipless fuck", Erica Jong's platonic ideal of sex, puresex, famously coined in her book Fear of Flying. Then let the stars be your safe guide to sexual satisfaction and success in our erotic Zodiac.

Aries *21 March–20 April*

Those born under the sign of the Ram have all that creature's raw energy and legendary horniness. They are hunters and warriors; they are competitive; they like to exert their physical and mental powers and seek to dominate, but may quickly lose interest if they believe that they have subjugated the object of their desires. In matters of sex, Aries are primeval, enthusiastic, dynamic, and experimental. Although they generally like to take they lead, they will react vigorously to a dare or a direct and unexpected sexual move made on them by others. They respond enthusiastically to the challenge of a new sexual position or an unusual location – the more illicit or outrageous the better. They have a taste for the spicier practices, for sex in public places, and above all for being the first to initiate their partner into a mind-blowing new experience. Aries of both sexes adore the excitement of the chase – often finding it more fulfilling than its conclusion. They abhor the dull and the routine, but will be passionately committed to a partner who continually tosses new sexual gauntlets in their path. However, while apparently brimming with confidence, they do need regular reassurance about the splendour of their sexual equipment and performance.

Monica Guevara (Contemporary)

Taurus 21 April–21 May

A typical Taurean is strong and patient, loyal, reliable, and perhaps also rather predictable and conservative. However, remember also that the Taurean is ruled by Venus, the planet of love and sensuousness. So, in matters of sex, Taureans are likely to be suspicious of the experimental and react with alarm at proposals to walk on the wilder side. On the other hand they love sex, and plenty of it, as part of their general indulgence in the pleasures of life. They respond strongly to the sight and feel of flesh. Nudity is a great turn on for them. So too is food, in which they have an inclination to over-indulge. Their pleasure in grazing is a natural lead-in to oral sex which has a strong appeal for this sign. They like sex in the great outdoors as well, but naked and lingering in a secluded spot rather than the snatched illicit public moment.

Gemini 22 May–21 June

Vivacious, spontaneous, and enthusiastic, generally guilt-free, and inclined to flirtatiousness, Geminians are stimulating virtuosi in matters of sex. But Gemini is one of the most romantic signs and so for Geminians sex and relationships are inextricably linked – the mind is their chief erogenous zone and they love to explore their partner's intellect and imagination as well as their body. They want affection, friendship, and mental stimulation as well as a lot of physical titillation. Geminis love their bodies being manipulated and handling their lover's body in return. Geminis are also great communicators; sex with them will not be a silent practice and definitely not something to do under cover of darkness. They want to see as well as feel everything, so it's morning sunlight or subdued and romantic lighting for them. Variety is certainly their spice of sexual life and they respond positively to an offer of immediate gratification. They are open to all sorts of experiments and novelties, but much prefer a brief, delicious experience, seized on the wing, than a long Tantric haul. And the twins are changeable personalities – what worked so well one day may bore them rigid the next.

Cancer 22 June–23 July

Cancerians are deeply affectionate, compassionate, and sensitive. Their love of domesticity and mothering (both giving it and receiving it) means that they are constantly seeking permanence and emotional security in their relationships. The romantic Cancerian is often a shy lover, hesitant to make the first move or to initiate sensual experimentation. However, once they have been reassured that they will not suffer rejection, they can be led gently into very voluptuous, if uncomplicated, loving, sexual relationships. Cancerians adore cuddling and stroking. Soft touches and gentle massages appeal strongly to them and Cancerian women respond powerfully to the stimulation of their breasts (and they are famously noisy when turned on). A final warning – remember that Cancerians are "crabby"; they can suffer periods of moodiness and jealousy, through which they will have to be coaxed with compliments and emotional comfort. They may be led back to sex through romantic sexual role-playing and a lot of kissing.

Leo 24 July–23 August

The royal beasts are extrovert, generous, warm-hearted, courageous, and enthusiastic. They can also be arrogant, vain, and selfish. This is a glamorous sign and Leos, bubbling with self-confidence, love to be the centre of attention socially and sexually. They will be physically demonstrative in public and private and engage in sex with the gusto that they demonstrate with all the good things of life. Leos enjoy domination in their sexual play and will have a tendency to keep the score and go for the record books in terms of versatility, frequency, and stamina. Their lovemaking must be superb – male Leos cannot countenance failure in the sexual arena, and if something goes wrong, they are deeply embarrassed and ashamed. Female Leos, while inclining to bossiness in public, expect their lovers to be very confident performers behind the bedroom door, or wherever else – Leos will go for it under any circumstances and be determined to show that they can do it better than anyone else ever has.

Virgo *24 August–23rd September*

Virgos are modest, considerate, and hardworking. They are definitely not attracted by the idea of the quickie or the one-night stand. They are often repulsed by the smells and messiness of unrestrained, raw sexual encounters. Shocking suggestions and full-frontal seduction techniques do not appeal to them, nor do improvised and impromptu sex. Sex should take place in the right place, usually the bedroom and certainly never in public, and at the right time, when all the other tasks of the day have been dealt with. Although quite prepared to envisage celibacy, if the circumstances for sex are not what they perceive as proper, Virgos are not necessarily asexual. Subtle and patient foreplay, running through the gamut of hugs and cuddles, kisses and touching, can release deep wells of lovingness. And they can learn to be very accomplished in sexual techniques, if they can be convinced that they are not doing anything naughty.

Libra *24 September–23 October*

Librans are strivers after balance and harmony in their lives. They are diplomatic, romantic, charming, easy-going, and gentle. But they have a dark side – they tend to be manipulative, self-regarding, and desperate for approval; they are compromisers and deceivers, indecisive and with a weakness for serial overlapping sexual relationships. Sexually, therefore, they are unlikely to indulge in the wild and spontaneous; they will seek to discover the keys to their partner's sexuality to charm and seduce them at the price of suppressing their own desires and indulging in fantasies, quite often acquiescent in nature – they so want to please. Though usually physically attractive and very interested in sex, when it comes to the act, Librans can prove insecure and confused as to their sexual identity, even though they maintain that confident Libran exterior. They are very responsive to sensual physical indulgence and have no particular hang-ups about experimentation and the juicier side of sex – especially if that will excite and delight their partner.

Scorpio *24 October–22 November*

Determined, forceful, emotional, intuitive, sexually magnetic, obsessed equally with eroticism and power, and sometimes quite sinister, Scorpios are probably the most passionate sign and also the most dangerous. Sex is one of their dominant life forces and they are deeply lustful and fascinated by the further shores of sexual experience, though as much to speculate and talk about them as to visit them. They will toy with all sorts of practices, cross-dressing, pornography, bondage, and domination; they are intrigued by the clandestine and the bizarre. The Scorpio demands total physical and emotional commitment and the idea of a light-hearted fling is inconceivable for them. While seeking the rapt commitment of their partners, they are fearful of showing weakness through overt affection or emotional commitment to others. A sexual relationship with a Scorpio can be a mind-blowing voyage of discovery, but also very exhausting physically and emotionally.

Sagittarius *23 November–21 December*

The enormous charm of Sagittarians lies in their positive, life-accepting, broadminded, impulsive, and idealistic philosophy. These are people who take life, and in particular sex, in both hands. To Sagittarians both love and sex are freewheeling enjoyable adventures; they are life's travellers, full of lust and also wanderlust whether geographical or sensual. Sagittarians are very tactile and all that hugging, stroking, and physical teasing makes them warm and sensuous lovers. Though they do not linger long over the foreplay, they have plenty of enthusiasm as well as endurance for the main event. No prudes, but they will respond much more to an energetic, wild, and free sexual romp than a dark exploration of the more arcane limits of sexual experience. They love physical activity of all kinds, and the Sagittarian will go for the quickie or the marathon with equal enthusiasm. Out-of-doors is fine; spontaneity regardless of location or consequences is a turn-on for them. Just do not expect too much physical finesse or emotional sophistication if you are a Sagittarian partner.

Capricorn

22 December–20 January

Capricorns are something of a contradiction. Outwardly they are conservative, reserved, ambitious, hardworking, and reliable. They are most unlikely to waste time on flirtatious dalliance or indulge in one-night stands, let alone an illicit workplace affair that would jeopardize their careers. On the other hand the goat is a by-word for horniness and Capricorns are reputed to have the strongest sexual appetite in the zodiac as well as legendary staying power. The tremendous drive that all too often makes them workaholics also makes them work at sex. They are driven to improve their performance and extend their sexual range. Goats are prepared to experiment and are always willing to learn, though they are not interested in the perverse or bizarre. Goats are also shy creatures to the point of secretiveness. They do not indulge in open displays of affection, much less public sexual play. However, what they lack in romance or sexual playfulness is more than compensated for by the voracity of their sexual appetites. Ultimately total concentration on their own and their partner's pleasure makes them outstanding lovers.

Monica Guevara (Contemporary)

Aquarius *21 January–19 February*

Aquarians are the free spirits of the zodiac – friendly, open-minded, unpossessive, visionary, and creative. But the other side of the coin is that they shy away from long-term commitments or open displays of emotion. They are attracted by the eccentric and their fascination with the great variety of human experience means that they love to speculate about the outer limits of sexual practice, to shock with way-out propositions, perhaps to indulge in voyeurism, and certainly in flights of psychedelic fantasizing. They are likely to be intrigued by sex toys and trinkets and arcane sexual knowledge. The Aquarian approach to sex is frequently more cerebral than sensual or passionate. They will go with the flow and will not be easily shocked, but they are not noted for a high level of libido. This, coupled with their fear of entanglements, means that Aquarians are not long-distance performers either emotionally or sexually.

Pisces *20 February–20 March*

Imaginative and intuitive, affectionate, compassionate, and selfless, those born under Pisces are gentle and empathetic personalities. They are very accepting of others and adaptable to their needs, but they are repulsed by harshness and cruelty and they are easily wounded. Having a tendency to be indecisive, dreamy, and not very energetic, in matters of sex they look to a strong, confident, uninhibited partner to lead the way, but through kindness and with no sense of coercion. Pisceans are quite self-critical, but are responsive to compliments and appreciative caresses. While quite ready to be seduced into sexual indulgence and tolerant of most sorts of experimentation, nothing that hints of pain or violence in sex appeals to the Piscean and they would far prefer waves of voluptuous sensuality to the passionate energy of raw sex. Being shy creatures, they prefer their sex at dusk or in darkness to bright sunlight or any sort of public display. Scented massages and languorous foreplay before coition itself and love and reassurance afterwards may be as important as the act itself for the romantic and other-worldly Piscean.

Resources

Book Publishers and Suppliers

The Erotic Print Society
EPS, 1 MADDOX STREET
LONDON W1S 2PZ

Tel (UK only): 0800 026 25 24 (freephone)
Fax: +44 (0) 207 437 3528
Email: eros@eroticprints.org
Website: www.eroticprints.org

(A free catalogue is available on request)

Paper Pleasures (antiquarian erotica)
Email: lesley@paperpleasures.bchip.com

Books

**Tijuana Bibles: Art and Wit in America's
Forbidden Funnies, 1930s–1950s**
Bob Adelman and Art Spiegelman (intro)
Simon & Schuster, 1997

**Sex Tips:
From Men Who Ride the Sexual Frontier**
Edited by Jo-Anne Baker
Fusion Press, 2001

Emily Ford's Pillow Book
The Erotic Print Society, 2002

**Divas and Lovers: The Erotic Art of Studio
Manassé.** Monika Faber
Universe Publishing, 1998

**The Good Ship Venus:
The Erotic Voyage of the Olympia Press**
John de St Jorre
Pimlico, 1994

**Three in Love: Ménage à Trois
From Ancient to Modern Times**
Barbara Foster, Letha Hadady, Michael Foster

Encyclopedia of Unusual Sex Practices
Brenda Love
Abacus, 1995

The Seductive Art of Japanese Bondage
Midori
Greenery Press, 2001

The Sexual Life of Catherine M.
Catherine Millet
Serpent's Tail, 2002

**The Naughty Bits,
from the Nerve.com column**
Jack Murnighan
Three Rivers Press, 2001

An Anthology of Erotic Verse
edited by Derek Parker
Constable and Co Ltd, 1980

Kokigami:
The Intimate Art of the Little Paper Costume
Burton Silver and Heather Busch
Angus & Robertson, 1991

Kokigami: Performance Enhancing
Adornments for the Adventurous Man
Burton Silver and Heather Busch
Ten Speed Press, 2000

Fetish: Fashion, Sex, & Power
Valerie Steele
Oxford University Press, 1996

The Complete Poems of John Wilmot, Earl of
Rochester
edited (and introduction) by David M Vieth
New Haven and London, Yale University Press, 1968

Top-Shelf Girls
Eric Wilkins (photographer)
The Erotic Print Society, 2002

The Complete Reprint of John Willie's Bizarre
Taschen, 1995

Magazines
The Erotic Review
1 Maddox Street, London W1S 2PZ
Tel: 020 7439 8999
Website: www.TheEroticReview.co.uk

Forum
Northern & Shell Tower, PO Box 381, City Harbour,
London, E14 9GL
Tel: 020 7308 5090
Email: forum@nasnet.co.uk

Desire
Mondance Media Limited, 1a Fentiman Road, London
SW8 1LD
Tel: 020 7820 8844
Website: www.desire.co.uk

Nerve.com

Skin Two Magazine
Unit 63, Abbey Business Centre, Ingate Place, London
SW8 3NS
Tel: 020 7498 5533
Website: www.skintwo.com/magazine/index.html

Websites
www.annsummers.com
www.skintwo.com/clothing
www.worldarterotica.com (art, literature)
www.sex-lexis.com
(dictionary, thesaurus, synoyms, quotations)

Credits

Illustrations

Illustrations on pages 10–12, 16–17, 26–27, 30–31, 44–45, 54–55, 65–67, 78–79, 82–83, 92–93, 96–97, 106–07, 117, 127, 150–51, 162–63, 171, 173–75, 186–87, 198–99, 201, 207, 209, 244–45, 256–57, 302–03, 311, and 316 courtesy of The Erotic Print Society and The Dupret Collection.

Werner Forman Archive: pages 138–139

Corbis: pages 40–41, 145, 292–93

Ediciones La Cupola: pages 268–69

Ray Leaning (© Ray Leaning/www.leaning.co.uk): pages 280–81

Housk Randall: pages 220–21

Terry Wakelin (www.olympia-press.co.uk): pages 232–33

Acknowledgements

The publisher would like to thank the following:

Paul Brown Ph.D and Christine Kell, authors of *The Good Sex Book*, Courage Books, 1997

Elizabeth Coldwell at *Forum* magazine for her kind permission to reproduce three articles

Nick Freeth for his help and advice on certain sources of material for this book

Paul Richardson for all his help and support

Serpent's Tail for the extract from *The Sexual Life of Catherine M.* on pages 166–69 by Catherine Millet, www.serpentstail.com

Charlie Wills and Peter Kennedy for the version of "The Game of Cards" on page 94, reproduced in *Folksongs of Britain & Ireland*, edited by Peter Kennedy, Cassell & Co, 1975

Ray Leaning (www.leaning.co.uk)

Terry Wakelin (www.olympia-press.co.uk)